The Collieries and Coalminers
of
STAFFORDSHIRE

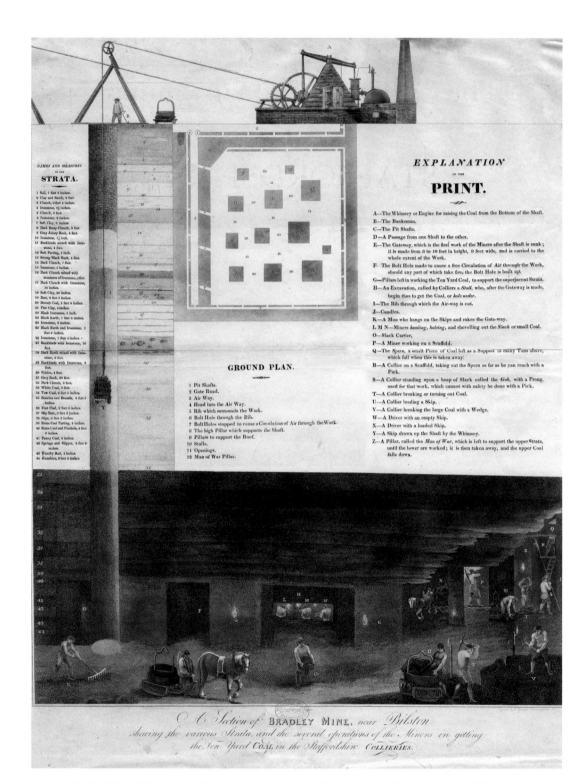

Bradley Mine, Bilston, engraved in 1806, showing a range of operations involved in mining the Thick Coal.

The Collieries and Coalminers
of
STAFFORDSHIRE

Richard Stone

Phillimore

2007

Published by
PHILLIMORE & CO. LTD
Chichester, West Sussex, England
www.phillimore.co.uk

ISBN 978-1-86077-455-3

Printed and bound in Great Britain

Contents

Acknowledgements

My thanks to David Bell, Ken Chackett, Yvonne Cooper, Professor Tom Elliott, Donald Frost, Mr C. Hammond, Monica Hudson, Peter Knowles, Alan Pilkington, Ray Smith, Albert Thompson, Miss L.M. Warham, J.T. Worgan, the Black Country Society, Cannock Chase Mining Historical Society, and to all the many individuals and organisations who have been helpful in the course of my research. I am particularly indebted to the Museum of Cannock Chase, South Derbyshire Mining Preservation Group, and those individuals who allowed me access to items, images and documents in their collections.

I am grateful also for assistance from the staff at Birmingham Central Library; the William Salt Library, Stafford; Staffordshire Record Office; Staffordshire Past-Track; Lichfield Record Office; Stoke-on-Trent City Archives; Dudley Metropolitan Borough Council Archives; Sandwell Community History and Archives Service; The Potteries Museum and Art Gallery; Newcastle-under-Lyme Borough Museum and Art Gallery; and The Coal Authority.

Illustrations: cover from the collection of the Museum of Cannock Chase, reproduced by permission of The Coal Authority; frontispiece, 3, 19, 70 reproduced courtesy of the Trustees of the William Salt Library, Stafford; 59, 108, 113, 117 reproduced courtesy of Newcastle-under-Lyme Borough Museum and Art Gallery; 46, 80, 107 reproduced courtesy of The Potteries Museum and Art Gallery; 38, 55, 58, 60, 61, 62, 63, 64, 66, 73, 77, 78, 82, 85, 86, 87, 89, 90, 101, 103, 104, 105, 111, 114, 116, 118, 119, 129, 130, 132, 134, 135, 136, 137, 138, 139, 142, 144, 145 reproduced courtesy of the Museum of Cannock Chase; 4, 22, 24, 57, 67, 75, 76, 96, 112, 131 reproduced courtesy Dudley Archives and Local History Service.

Every effort has been made to establish and contact copyright owners but in one or two instances this has not proved possible.

Endpapers are sections reproduced from the 1947 (One-Inch) maps of the Ordnance Survey.

Author photograph by Karen Lanchester.

Special thanks to my daughter, Helen Stone, for drawings.

List of Illustrations

Frontispiece: Bradley Mine, Bilston, engraved in 1806 and showing a range of operations involved in mining the Thick Coal

Land, Lords and Earthly Riches

Scratch the surface of Staffordshire and you will find coal. Local folklore tells of a gravedigger at St John's Church, Kates Hill in Dudley who was accustomed to digging out coal equivalent to the space needed for a coffin from a shallow vein running through the churchyard. Workmen laying sewers in the streets of Edwardian Bilston cut coal from the trenches they dug.

Seams of coal formed in layers from plant material deposited in the Carboniferous period some 300 million years ago. The Midland Barrier, a geological feature marking a prehistoric shoreline, crosses Wales and England from west to east, passing immediately south of Staffordshire. North of this belt a sub-tropical climate and river-fed swamps were favourable biochemical conditions, producing first peat and then coal. A fossil forest illustrating the process, primeval trunks and roots graphically petrified where they had fallen, was revealed during opencast working near Wolverhampton in 1844. Apart from a fringe of millstone grit in the north east of the county and isolated pockets of older pre-Carboniferous rocks in the south, few areas of Staffordshire are without an

1   *Coal was discovered beneath the streets of Bilston by workmen digging trenches to lay sewer pipes in 1906.*

2   *Geology divides North Staffordshire, Cannock Chase and South Staffordshire into three distinct coalfields.*

underpinning of coal. Geological rifts and fault lines break the strata, dividing North Staffordshire, Cannock Chase and South Staffordshire into three distinct coalfields. Local authority reorganisation in 1974 transferred a swathe of Staffordshire from Wolverhampton to Dudley into a newly formed West Midlands Metropolitan County. To maintain the integrity of the South Staffordshire coalfield this arbitrary redrawing of boundaries is ignored and the area treated as 'honorary' Staffordshire.

South Staffordshire's coalfield is split by the Russell Hall Faults stretching beneath Dudley from Rowley Regis to Upper Gornal, and detached from Cannock Chase field by the Bentley Faults. Water-bearing New Red Sandstone, red marl and pebble beds overlie compact coal measures. Below is Old Red Sandstone surfacing in isolated outcrops around Dudley and in the Walsall area. North of the Bentley Faults, drifts of thick, glacial boulder clay hindered early mining of shallow seams. Concealed measures running north-east from Birmingham to Rugeley between the Vigo and Clayhanger (or Eastern Boundary) Faults in the east and the Huntington, Mitre and Bushbury Faults in the west, lay deeply buried. Crosscut and split by Hammerwich Fault and a geological rift known as the Rising Sun Trough, this concealed coal remained unexploited until the late 19th century. Folds divide the main Potteries field in the north of the county from smaller beds at Cheadle, Goldsitch Moss and Shaffalong. A finger of coal extending beneath Tamworth more properly belongs to the North Warwickshire coalfield.

In South Staffordshire, a dozen or more separate seams coalesce in a uniquely rich bed known as the 'Ten Yard Seam' or 'Thick Coal'. Nowhere else in Great Britain has coal of such quality and quantity been available at relatively shallow depth.

Veins within the Thick Coal were given their own names by miners. Although there were variations from area to area, among those in widespread use in the 17th century, starting from the upper layer and working down, were: Dun-Dicks, Roof or Top Floor, Top or Over Slipper, sometimes known as Spires, Jays, Lambs, Kitt's, Tow or Heath, Benches, Brazils or the Kernel, Bottom-Slipper or Foot Coal, Slip-bat, John Coal, Stone Coal or Long Coal, Great Patch, Springs or Sawyer, Slippers, and the Humphries or Bottom Bench. Above the Thick Coal and even closer to the surface, a separate thin seam of superior, fast-burning household coal called the 'Brooch' was largely ignored until the late 18th century. Below the main measures, a lower quality vein identified by the name 'Heathing-coal', or more commonly 'Heathen', was mined to access underlying beds of iron ore. Approaching the Bentley Faults the Thick Coal seams begin to separate. Outcrops in the Upper Gornal area were known as the 'Flying Reed Coal'. To the north, beyond the faults, the seams diverge even further and plunge much deeper.

In the north of the county, fault lines fold some of the thickest workable coal seams in Britain deep into the earth. Quality here is more variable but the best is of very high grade. Among the named seams, Bullhurst, Crabtree or Four Foot Mine, Ragman, Cockshead, Holly Lane, Bowling Alley and Great Row are among the most prized. From the mid-15th century the Great Row seam was in demand for firing pottery kilns. Holly Lane coal was favoured for domestic use. In later years the Bowling Alley seam proved ideal for smelting and for firing steam engines, the Crabtree measures for coking.

Accessible outcrops were mined from at least the 13th century and probably much earlier. Indications of coal mining

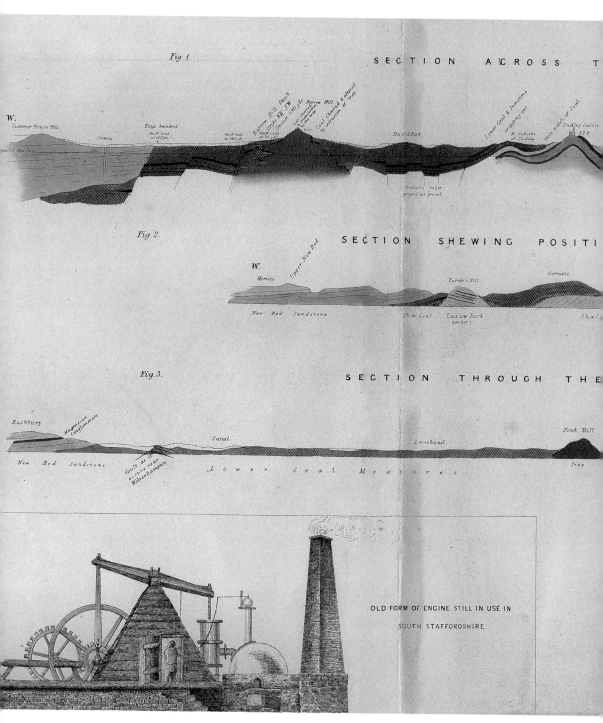

Fig. 1. SECTION ACROSS T

Fig. 2. SECTION SHEWING POSITI

Fig. 3. SECTION THROUGH THE

OLD FORM OF ENGINE STILL IN USE IN

SOUTH STAFFORDSHIRE.

3 *Geological section across the South Staffordshire coalfield showing the Thick Coal, concealed measures east of the Boundary Fault, and lower seams. Inset is a Newcomen-style atmospheric steam engine of the type first demonstrated near Tipton in 1712.*

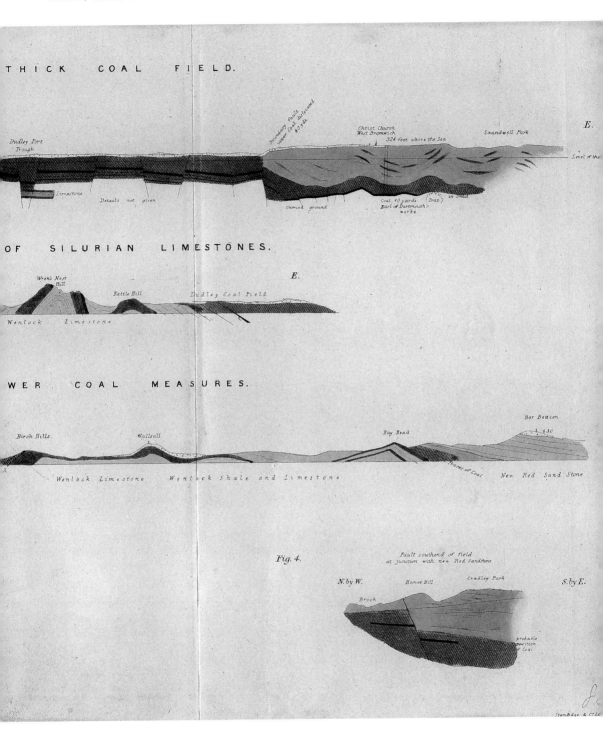

THICK COAL FIELD.

OF SILURIAN LIMESTONES.

WER COAL MEASURES.

Fig. 4.

4   *Thick Coal, Baggeridge Colliery, c.1900. A number of different seams coalesce to form the uniquely rich Thick Coal measures of South Staffordshire. With seams 30ft deep, miners frequently had recourse to simple scaffolding and ladders at the face.*

5   *Figurative metal sculpture in Baggeridge Country Park set on a foundation block of the old pithead framework. Commissioned from artist Steve Field in 1998 to mark the 30th anniversary of the closure of Baggeridge Colliery, the last working mine in South Staffordshire, it was made in Dudley by D.R. Harvey and shows a miner working the Thick Coal.*

were revealed in the late 1950s during excavation of a second-century site at Holditch, north of Newcastle-under-Lyme. Roman pottery kilns, similar to a first-century example discovered at Trent Vale, may have been coal-fired. Biddulph derives its name from 'by the delph', meaning 'by the diggings'. It is recorded as *Bidolf* in Domesday Book, suggesting mining activity of some description was taking place in the immediate area before the Norman Conquest. Coal and iron ore, along with fireclay, occurred in adjacent beds. In medieval times, ironstone was the more important commodity. Iron ore was smelted in small clay stacks using hand-operated bellows to raise the temperature sufficiently to produce a bloom of metal. Manorial court rolls assess a Tunstall coal mine as worth 14s. 8d. in 1282. Adjacent

ironstone workings are valued at forty times that amount. Acrid smoke and a variety of gases released made burning coal unpleasant. It was poor man's fuel, quarried from the surface with picks and shovels.

Early documentary sources mention mining in the late 13th century at Sedgley (1273), Kingswinford (1291), Shelton (1297, where a mine is assessed as worth 10s. a year), Cannock (1297, valued at 48s. a year), Rushall and Walsall. In the early 14th century, records confirm pits near Longdon (1305), Wednesbury (1315), Norton-in-the-Moors (1316), Horton (1317) and Keele (1333). A pit on Lee Field was providing the Cistercian monks of Abbey Hulton with coal in the 14th century. Manorial accounts for the Longdon Estate on Cannock Chase, owned by the bishops of Lichfield, show

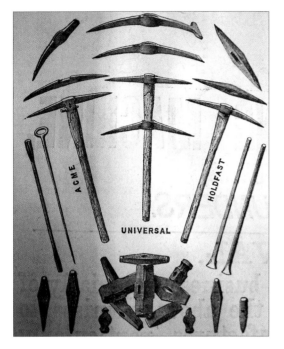

6 *Selection of late 19th-century picks, hammers, prickers, rammers and scrapers, hand tools that remained in use into the modern era.*

five separate mines in 1305 rented out at six pence per pick. The records make clear activity was seasonal, largely carried out from spring to autumn.

Landowners and those they licensed to quarry on their estates, freeholders and copyholders exercising privileges of common based on customary rights, and others with initiative, if more doubtful claims, all plundered Staffordshire's mineral resources. Basic hand tools, a wheelbarrow, fitness and the will to work hard were the key requirements. Crop damage and digging without licence are regular charges brought by various lords of the manor against their tenants in 14th-century court rolls for the shire. The number of disputes suggests extensive activity, beyond what might be expected if coal were being dug for purely personal use. Accessibility and minimal capital outlay allowed enterprising, determined

young men to set up in business part-time, supplementing their income as farmers, craftsmen or agricultural labourers by supplying coal to local small industrial and domestic customers. Principles of custom and practice underpin the English legal system. As coal increased in value, landowners attempting to reassert mineral rights encountered courts inclined to recognise and uphold liberties established by centuries of tradition. In South Staffordshire it became standard practice to insert a clause in property leases that landowners were entitled to half of any profits earned from coal and ironstone. By the beginning of the 15th century more equitable arrangements were sought. Landowners and freehold tenants were forced to reach mutually acceptable agreements before mining operations started.

In 1549 Amblecote Manor Court upheld the lord's right to mine on property held by tenants with the rider that compensation must be paid for any damage caused. Awards were based on a recommendation made by two manorial tenants, one nominated by either party. Numerous licences issued by the court show mining increasing, and records catalogue attempts to regulate productivity. In 1550 the manorial court at Amblecote set a limit or 'turn' defined in terms of cartloads and horse consignments at each pit. Fines were enforced for any infringement. It was more than two decades before the court loosened its controlling grip.

The Paget family along with the lords of Dudley, Enville and Stafford were among the first major landowners to begin systematic mining of coal on their estates. Sir William Paget acquired former Church property on Cannock Chase after the Reformation. Coal from the 'Old Park seam' at Beaudesert Park, where he made his home, was sent to help make Mary,

7   *Beaudesert Hall in its 18th-century prime. The Paget family developed extensive coal mining interests on their Cannock Chase estate. The hall was demolished in 1934.*

Queen of Scots' enforced confinement at nearby damp and draughty Tutbury Castle more comfortable. The Crown confiscated Beaudesert after Thomas and Charles Paget were caught up in the Throckmorton Plot and fled to France in 1583. It was twenty years before Thomas's heir had the family estates restored. In the meantime the 'veins of coal "called pitt cole, stone cole and sea cole"' were leased to Gilbert Wakering of Bloxwich, who had recently acquired the lordship of Wombourne. This brief interlude aside, the Pagets managed their own collieries directly, other landowners preferring to rent out works. In the mid-16th century Sir John Harpur leased a mine at Quarnford for an annual rent of £12 and two fat hens.

Writing in his *Itinerary*, undertaken around 1540, John Leland noted numerous smiths working in Birmingham who 'have

yren out of Staffordshire and Warwickshire and see-coale out of Staffordshire'. Coal was used to fire forges for small-scale metalworking but contained too many impurities for satisfactory smelting of ore. High amounts of sulphur produced brittle pig iron. Around 1560, when Lord Paget of Beaudesert built what was almost certainly the first blast furnace in the Midlands on the edge of Cannock Chase, charcoal was the preferred fuel. Paget had been ambassador to France where waterpower was already being used to inject a powerful blast of air into increasingly larger stacks.

William Wilkes, a specialist with a track record of success in finding hidden measures in the Leicestershire coalfield, was hired by the Paget estate in 1600 to pinpoint the most promising sites. 'Borers' used iron augurs, bouncing and twisting the rods to drill through intermediate rock

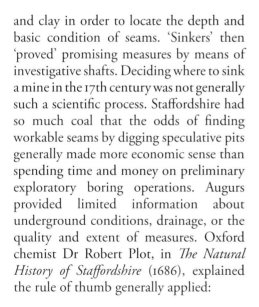

8 *Hand-operated sinking machine, c.1870. Weights held the machine in position.*

9 *Portable quarrying machine, c.1870, with adjustable legs, capable of drilling at various angles.*

and clay in order to locate the depth and basic condition of seams. 'Sinkers' then 'proved' promising measures by means of investigative shafts. Deciding where to sink a mine in the 17th century was not generally such a scientific process. Staffordshire had so much coal that the odds of finding workable seams by digging speculative pits generally made more economic sense than spending time and money on preliminary exploratory boring operations. Augurs provided limited information about underground conditions, drainage, or the quality and extent of measures. Oxford chemist Dr Robert Plot, in *The Natural History of Staffordshire* (1686), explained the rule of thumb generally applied:

> For finding of coal, if in a place where never any have bin discover'd, they first consult the springs if any near, to see whether they can find any coal water i.e. an acid water having a car, or yellow sediment: above ground they look for a smut as they call it, i.e. a friable black earth …

Dud Dudley, illegitimate son of Edward, Lord Dudley and local miner's daughter Elizabeth Tomlinson, became an industrialist of renown. In the 1620s he professed to have used pit coal to make glass in furnaces set up near his home at Green Lodge, Wombourne. He later claimed success in smelting iron using coal. While Dudley's account (*Metallum Martis* written in 1665) of the experiments carried out at his works reveals in-depth understanding of smelting processes, it does not go into detail about the methods employed. It is possible that he was keen to protect any commercial advantage.

10   *Ornamental items carved out of densely textured pieces of coal have been popular since the 17th century.*

Twenty years later, Robert Plot was able to write of Staffordshire's coal that it was:

> Fit for most other uses, but not for melting, fineing, and refining of iron which it cannot be brought to doe.

Surface outcrops contain considerably less sulphur than deeper measures and it may have been from this source Dudley drew supplies for his experiments. An experiment carried out at the Black Country Museum, using a specially constructed replica of a 17th-century furnace fired by partly carbonised outcropping coal, proved smelting was achievable although the quality of iron was below that required for the manufacture of durable edge tools.

During the Civil War, Parliamentarian forces besieging a Royalist contingent dug in behind strong fortifications at Cathedral Close, Lichfield in 1643, called upon the skills of Staffordshire's colliers. Fifty miners burrowed beneath the defences to create a breach and help bring a potentially protracted stand-off to a rapid conclusion.

Col is an Old English word and in medieval times was shorthand for charcoal. Coal in the modern sense was differentiated as 'pit coal', 'stone coal' or 'sea coal', a term that most likely originated in London where supplies were shipped from the north east of England. Before chimneys became common in the mid-16th century, smoke from open indoor hearths was left to find its own way out, escaping through gaps in roofing or through louvres inserted for the purpose in the gable ends of buildings. In an essay on the mineralogy of south-west Staffordshire written for Stebbing Shaw's *The History and Antiquities of Staffordshire*, published in 1798, James Keir compares the quality favourably with coal from Newcastle-on-Tyne:

> It kindles more readily, and makes a pleasanter fire, requires less trouble in management, and makes less dust [and] is also a good coal for all kinds of metallic processes.

Bituminous coal, rich in volatile hydrocarbons that burned brightly, was used domestically to provide both heat and light and was called 'cannel' or 'candle coal'. Densely textured cannel could be carved to make fashionable knick-knacks such as inkwells or candlesticks. Polished slices were inserted as a contrast to flesh-coloured alabaster decorating the choir of Lichfield Cathedral. Robert Plot describes how an image of James II carved from cannel mined on Lord Paget's Cannock Chase estate 'resembled him well', the final polish administered with 'sealskin and rushes'. Plot also describes the care taken in laying coal fires, observing:

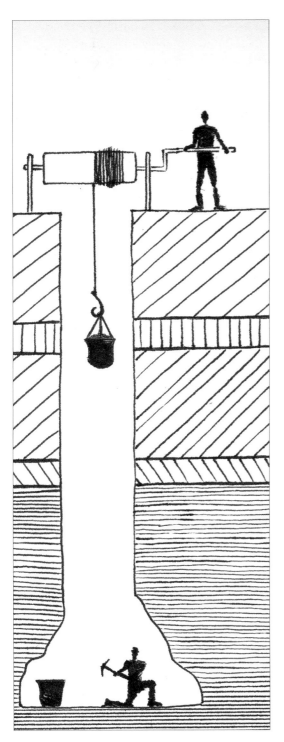

11   Bell-pits were a two-man operation. A narrow shaft was sunk into the seam and coal raised in a basket using a windlass.

If they would have it burn slow (as the poorer and thriftier sort of people will) they lay it flat ways upon the fire, as it lay before in the bed or measure; but if they would have it burn quick and flame clear (as the gentry commonly will) they surbed it, i.e. set it edgeways the cleaving way next the fire, by which means it so easily admits it, that it presently flames as bright as a candle, whence perhaps not unlikely it may receive its name.

Softer, open-textured coal, used in blacksmiths' forges, was known as 'peacock', a reference to flaring blue and yellow hues given off as it burned and fancifully thought to resemble a peacock's colourful tail.

Opencast mining of outcrops or 'bassets', and drift mines pursuing seams into hillsides along tunnels called 'footrails' or 'footrills', was followed by the sinking of vertical shafts to reach seams lying up to thirty or forty feet beneath the surface. Men worked in pairs, one at the bottom of the shaft and the other hauling the coal out with a rope and basket, most usually a wooden skip woven from hazel rods. A 'basket' became the standard measure in which coal was traded. A dozen baskets weighed a little over a ton. Shafts were typically around 4ft 6in. diameter. Tunnelling sideways from the foot of the shaft along the seam on either side continued until the roof threatened to collapse. These workings became known as 'bell-pits' or 'beehives' from their characteristic shape. Tools included picks (called 'pikes' in some areas), wedges, mattocks and square-bladed, iron-edged wooden shovels. Picks used for coal cutting were lighter than those used for stonework or shaft sinking. Narrow, tapered blades around 18 inches from tip to tip, gave extra reach when undercutting a face or 'holing out'.

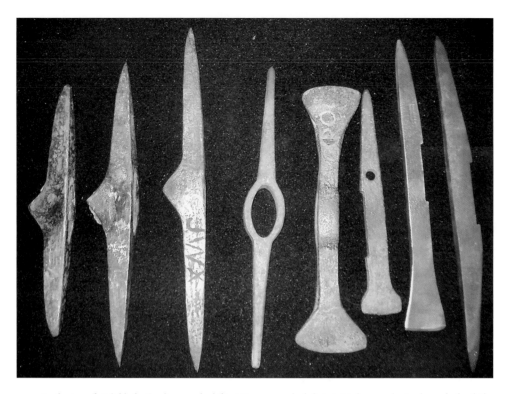

12   *A selection of pick blades (earliest on the left). Miners scratched their initials on tools. At the end of a shift, picks were dismantled and left underground. Shaft and socket were locked on a tool rod or clip and the blade and pick key (essential to lock the blade in place) buried nearby.*

As the industry expanded, deeper and deeper shafts were sunk, with adits providing basic ventilation and drainage. Basic timber shuttering extended the area that could be safely worked. Winding apparatus and horse gins were introduced to enable coal to be raised more efficiently. Gins had a horizontally mounted rope drum that was turned either clockwise or counter-clockwise by a horse (or horses) following a circular track to raise and lower baskets in the shaft. Even these more ambitious projects were affordable enterprises for yeomen farmers and lesser gentry either individually or in partnership.

Staffordshire's woodland came under increasing pressure to supply charcoal for furnaces. A sustainable cycle required two thousand acres of coppice to keep one small blast furnace supplied and resources were unable to keep pace with increasing industrialisation and rising production. It was not only iron forges stimulating demand. Pottery, glass manufacture, saltworks, brickmaking, brewing and malting were also growing local industries. All required constant supplies of fuel and demand for coal began to soar. Many Staffordshire iron manufacturers temporarily transferred their operations into neighbouring Shropshire where the well-wooded Severn Valley remained largely unexploited and costs were lower. It was at his Coalbrookdale works, established in 1709, that Abraham Darby reduced overheads even more by developing the use of coke for smelting iron, in the process producing a low-sulphur metal suitable for the manufacture of thin

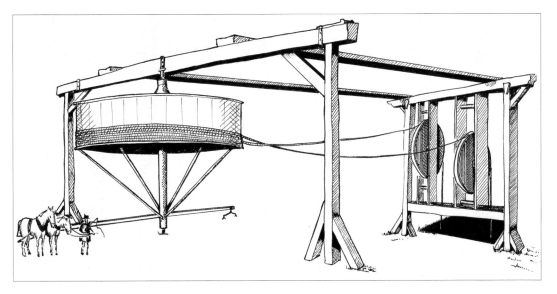

13 *Simple but effective whimsey or 'whim' gins were in use into the 20th century. Pulley attachments enabled horses to be kept well away from the mouth of the shaft. Drums, typically around 10 feet in diameter delivered more lifting power than smaller cog and rung gins.*

14 *Cog and rung gin. Teeth engage to turn the winding drum.*

castings. Darby, born in Sedgley, may have drawn some clues from Dud Dudley's experiments half-a-century earlier. The two were related, Darby's grandfather having married Dudley's niece, Margaret Parkshouse.

Controlled roasting of coal, at temperatures high enough to burn off impurities in the matrix without igniting the carbon content, produced an ideal fuel for use in blast furnaces. Relatively soft-textured 'Heathen' seams proved particularly suitable for coking. In 1773 Joseph Jesson and Company of West Bromwich successfully used coke to refine pig iron into high quality wrought iron and their methods were soon widely copied.

By-products of the coking process, such as coal tar, pitch, and most importantly gas, soon established spin-off industries. William Murdoch pioneered the use of coal gas for lighting in the 1790s. Commercial potential was demonstrated in 1802 when Murdoch lit the Soho Works of Boulton and Watt with coal gas, and Birmingham celebrated the Treaty of Amiens with gas-lit illuminations. Peace in Europe was short-lived, but within 25 years Birmingham and Staffordshire Gas Light Company had opened works at Swan Village, West Bromwich and the British Gaslight Company was supplying the Potteries from gasworks in Lower Bedford Street, Hanley. By the 1850s, coal gas was common in factories, widely used for street lighting, and domestic demand was growing. Giant cylindrical holders where gas was stored and pressurised soon became a familiar feature of the urban landscape.

The natural interdependence of coal and iron as twin enterprises in Staffordshire was strengthened by the use of coke, boosting iron working in the second half of the 18th century. John 'Iron Mad' Wilkinson set up a state-of-the-art blast furnace at his Bradley works in 1767, and by the 1790s coal had completely replaced charcoal in smelting. The *Universal Directory* recorded of Bilston:

> Here are very considerable mines of coal, ironstone, quarry stone and clay, all of excellent quality. The quantity of coal got in this township may be conjectured from this circumstance, that the works of John Wilkinson, Esq. alone, consume 800 tons per week.

In the same entry, the *Directory* goes on to inform readers of an underground fire that had been burning for over three decades:

> It is in fact a bed of coal which is burning, about four feet thick, and about eight or ten yards deep, to which the air has free access, by reason of the thick or main coal having been dug from under it.

By the close of the 18th century the combined appetite of all the blast furnaces in the Black Country exceeded three-quarters of a million tons of coal annually. Domination of the market gave the ironmasters control and enabled them to dictate prices.

Nationally, demand for coal continued to rise with growing industrialisation. Staffordshire, a provincial backwater with some of the worst roads in the country, was unable to take advantage. Transport was a problem even within the county, many roads becoming impassable for weeks at a time in winter. Hauling coal in sledges and carts made matters worse. Robert Plot had reported in 1686 that the roads around Wednesbury, Sedgley and Dudley were 'incessantly worn by the carriage of coale'. William Wardle, generations of whose family leased mines in the Goldsitch Moss area from the Harpur lords of the manor, was forced to carry out repairs on a damaged road from his pits at Knotbury in the early-18th century. Matters improved only slightly when the River Trent Navigation was extended upriver as far as Burton-on-Trent in 1712. An initial overland journey was still necessary to reach the new wharf. Consequently, trade was restricted until the coming of the canal age ended Staffordshire's relative isolation and opened up new markets. Work on the 'Grand Trunk', conceived as the first step in an inland waterway system designed to link Hull, Liverpool, Manchester, London

15   *Wedges used for breaking up large lumps of coal or stone. A hole or 'stomp' was made with a pick before inserting a wedge and striking it with a hammer. Young miners were advised, 'Always make a good stomp for your wedge, my lad.'*

and Bristol, began in 1766. Chief sponsor was Burslem potter Josiah Wedgwood.

Following the contours of the Trent valley, the Trent and Mersey Canal, as it became known, ran straight through the North Staffordshire coalfield and skirted Cannock Chase. At the time, it was the most ambitious engineering project ever undertaken in Europe. Driving through Harecastle Hill, Kidsgrove was the major challenge. It took 11 years and provided a snapshot of Staffordshire's mineral richness. Extensive deposits of ironstone and 26 separate seams of coal were revealed as work progressed. Coal was mined from shafts leading directly from the tunnel deep into the hillside. Until 1827, when Thomas Telford completed a wider channel alongside incorporating a towpath, barges had to be 'legged' through the narrow one-and-a-half mile passage.

The Trent and Mersey Canal put Staffordshire at the hub of a national waterway network. Within the next few years the Staffordshire and Worcestershire Canal, Dudley Canal and the Birmingham Canal were completed, with several branches linking to pits and towns in South Staffordshire. Cheaper transport had a dramatic effect on the price of coal, stimulating demand even further. But trade remained predominantly local. In Birmingham the price per ton fell by a third from 13s. to 8s. John, 2nd Viscount Dudley and Ward, recognised the opportunity and set about systematically developing mining on his extensive estates stretching from Kingswinford and Rowley Regis through Dudley to Sedgley and Tipton. He was a shareholder in the Staffordshire and Worcestershire Canal and promoted branches linking his works via Dudley

16 *Victorian Bilston. Constant firing resulted in the flames of blast furnaces lighting Black Country nights.*

Castle tunnel to the Birmingham and Dudley canals.

In 1775 Sir Nigel Gresley and his son were granted permission to dig a canal from their pits at Apedale into Newcastle-under-Lyme on condition that local residents were supplied with coal at a fixed price for two consecutive 21-year terms. It was a deal that proved unsustainable. By 1796, the start of the second term, the price cap was broken, and in 1812 supplies began to run out. Local rioting threatened to spiral out of control until arrangements for alternative supplies resolved the situation.

In 1777 the Caldon Canal ended the relative isolation of the mines around Cheadle in the Staffordshire Moorlands. As the waterway network expanded in mid-county, collieries at Brereton installed tramways which used horses to pull open waggons on rails to the nearest access point. Elsewhere, spurs were cut linking collieries directly to the waterways. Canal companies were soon operating as independent coal merchants. 'Joey-boats' carried coal from the Cannock Chase collieries to Saltley Cut, Bordesley via the Cannock Extension and Anglesey Branch canals. From Birmingham, the Grand Union Canal led to London and Oxford. By 1815 the first steam-powered coal barges were operating between Birmingham and London, bringing down transportation costs and opening up further markets. The Staffordshire and Worcestershire Canal gave Staffordshire access to Bristol, Gloucester and south west England. Stafford Colliery continued to use canal transport until the mid-20th century.

Industrial growth came at an environmental cost. Visiting Bilston in 1843, the Midland Mining Commission reported an industrial landscape of:

> two-storeyed houses interspersed with blazing furnaces, heaps of burning coal in process of coking, piles of ironstone calcining forges, pit banks and engine

17 *Expansion of the pottery industry in North Staffordshire stimulated demand for coal. A constant pall of smoke hung over the Five Towns.*

chimneys beside intersecting canals crossing each other at various levels, and the small remaining patches of surface soil are occupied by irregular fields of grass and corn intermingled with heaps of refuse of mines, or from the slag of blast furnaces.

Constant firing ensured the furnaces were never idle. American Henry Adams wrote graphically of 'the plunge into darkness lurid with flames' he experienced during a visit in 1858. 'Black by day and red by night,' wrote Elihu Burritt, United States consul to Birmingham, in his *Walks in the Black Country and its Green Border-land.* Published in 1868, Burritt's work helped popularise the description 'Black Country', an imprecise but instantly understood shorthand first noted in 1834, embracing the industrial conurbation of the exposed South Staffordshire coalfield. In North Staffordshire, though less voracious consumers, the distinctive bottle-shaped

kilns of the pottery industry, eventually more than two thousand of them working around the clock, were also increasing demand, their associated chimneys lighting up the night with an eerie glow and casting a pall of smoke.

Lord Dudley was influential in quarterly meetings of fellow coal owners in South Staffordshire who met to regulate prices and miners' wages. The sheer scale of mining operations, the richness of coal seams, and diversity of business interests insulated the Dudley Estate from the worst effects of economic fluctuations that were such a problem for the more typical, small, South Staffordshire mining enterprises. But Lord Dudley's mines were every bit as inefficient. Small shafts were sunk and new mines opened indiscriminately. William (3rd Viscount Dudley and Ward, and from 1827 1st Earl of Dudley) was keen to take full advantage of opportunities offered by the canal network. In an effort to inject a more businesslike approach, Charles Beaumont,

18 *Dudley Castle, neglected and ruinous in the mid-18th century, by which time Lord Dudley and Ward had moved to the more comfortable and fashionable surroundings of Himley Hall.*

a mining engineer from Newcastle-on-Tyne, author of an influential *Treatise on the Coal Trade* was recruited as mineral agent. Beaumont's brief was to increase profitability. To do, as he put it:

> the best which can with equity be done for his lordship's concerns … raising the greatest quantity and on the lowest terms.

Beaumont began work in 1797 and lost little time in making changes. Mine owners tended to operate at arm's length from day to day operations. A charter master known as a 'butty' acted as middleman. An agreement or 'charter' was typically for a set period of time. Butties were paid by the 'ton', a flexible measure rather than a fixed weight, similar to the 'basket' of earlier times. Expected yield and the price per ton for various grades of coal were specified. Under Beaumont's

direction, a new standard charter was drawn up defining more clearly the butties' responsibility for efficient underground working. By agreeing to pay for small broken coal or 'cobbles', currently treated as waste, Beaumont re-negotiated a 21 cwt ton arrangement to 26 cwt. His plan was to sort and grade all the coal produced, making it easier for dealers to meet specific customer requirements. By guaranteeing quality, premium prices were obtained for the best coal, while at the lower end of the market demand was created for previously unsaleable cobbles as cheap fuel.

Increased competitiveness was secured by fixing prices directly with dealers rather than allowing a number of different canal carriers to set their own profit margins. Horse-drawn railways, the first in South Staffordshire to use metal tracks, were laid from pithead to canal. Weighing equipment was installed at every wharf. Ventilation was improved to allow more extensive

19 *Beam engine at work in South Staffordshire in the early 19th century, pumping floodwater into a reservoir and winding two shafts. After loading, flat skips were 'banded' and chained before being raised.*

underground working from a single shaft and remove the need for continually sinking new pits. Boring operations to test the depth and character of new seams were improved, and instead of using percussion augurs, Beaumont developed a rotary drill tipped with a circular cutting surface of natural carbon crystals, similar in hardness to diamonds. Larger shafts were divided down the centre with a wooden brattice combining both upcast and downcast and saving the expense of sinking two smaller shafts. Instead of the traditional Staffordshire 'square work' method of extraction, Beaumont instituted new systems underground. Cutting longer sections in layers working from the bottom up increased efficiency and reduced the amount of cobbles produced. By ensuring sumps were sunk to an optimum depth, and driving connections between pits, the effectiveness of pumping operations was so improved that one steam engine was able to accomplish what had previously taken four. Seasonal closures due to flooding were largely averted.

Beaumont's achievement was little short of a revolution. In less than two years radical change had transformed Lord Dudley's operations. Costs were reduced and production increased. Coal from the Dudley Estate dominated the local market and was competitive via the canal network as far as Oxford and London. Beaumont's ambitious vision extended further. He proposed to abolish the butty system, dismiss the charter masters, create a management structure and employ miners directly, but this break with tradition proved a step too far. Presentation failed, misinformation and rumours circulated, and it was claimed miners brought in from north east England because of a shortage of manpower would displace local workers. There were violent demonstrations and machinery was sabotaged. Threats to burn down Lord Dudley's residence at Himley Hall were taken seriously. To calm the situation, Beaumont had to go. Without him, the mines soon lapsed back into inefficiency. In 1836, nine years after the death of the Earl of Dudley, who left no heir, with the estate temporarily in the hands of trustees led by Edward Littleton, a report commissioned to investigate the state of the mines was highly critical of the estate's mine agents, concluding:

20   *Himley Hall. Viscount Dudley and Ward added the grand south front to an existing central block in 1824-7. The hall was sold to become the West Midlands Divisional headquarters of the National Coal Board in 1947. Acquired by Wolverhampton and Dudley Borough Council in 1966, it now belongs to Dudley Metropolitan Borough Council.*

21   *Sir Edward John Littleton (1791-1863), Trustee of Lord Dudley's estate and a leading Staffordshire coal owner. As MP for Stafford he sponsored a Bill to control 'Truck' arrangements and was created Lord Hatherton in 1835. In 1842 he was involved in a celebrated court case over mineral rights on Cannock Chase with the Marquis of Anglesey.*

About 15 cannot write or read … 25 who are educated men: the rest, say about 20, are in a sort of intermediate state as regards intelligence.

Few agents maintained plans of the pits for which they were responsible. Instead, mine bailiffs were expected either to keep a mental note of underground workings, or else to use pegs to give a crude indication on the surface of what was happening below ground. Richard Smith, one of the authors of the report, was appointed to restructure the Earl of Dudley's colliery empire. Under his guidance, detailed financial accounting systems were introduced. Effort was concentrated on the collieries producing the best returns. Less profitable mines, including Coneygre, Dudley Moor, Gornalwood and others, were leased out, typically for 21 years and with strict conditions attached. Employees

22   *Miners and pony at the pithead, Himley Colliery, c.1900.*

were put on a more permanent basis under competent, salaried managers. Productivity and profitability once more improved.

Before the 19th century, mining of the compact Cannock Chase field was largely confined to Beaudesert Park and outcrops in the north east, and to a square of land in the south containing Essington, Bloxwich, Cheslyn Hay and Great Wyrley. Lord Shrewsbury's No. 1 Pit, Brick Kiln Colliery, sunk in 1820 near Brereton on land leased from Henry Paget, 1st Marquis of Anglesey, was probably the first mine east of the Clayhanger/Vigo Boundary Faults.

Wrangles over mineral rights between tenants and landowners continued into the 19th century. The law was far from clear. Interpretation based on manorial custom and practice led to different legal decisions affecting adjacent manors. Freehold tenants generally had the right to mine coal for their own use or for sale, and could sublet their rights. Copyholders, a form of tenure rooted in the feudal system, might have the right to mine coal for personal use but depending on manorial custom required

permission for commercial operations. Lord Hatherton sank a pit at Rumer Hill within the Rugeley and Cannock domain of the Marquis of Anglesey, believing he needed only to secure the agreement of copyhold tenants. The courts, 'contrary to expectations' according to the *Worcester Chronicle*, took a different view and in a celebrated case of 1842 awarded the Marquis a share of the proceeds. Hatherton closed the mine rather than pay royalties. Sir Thomas Talfourd, presiding, amused himself by recording court proceedings in rhyme. In his personal notes of the case, Talfourd has Sir Thomas Wilde, one of the most famous advocates of the day, opening for the Defence:

> The noble Plaintiff thro' his ancient rolls,
> Will find no entry giving him the coals.

Yearly output in South Staffordshire peaked in 1865 with some 400 collieries collectively producing around nine million tons. By the 1870s output from the Earl of Dudley's collieries alone exceeded one million tons

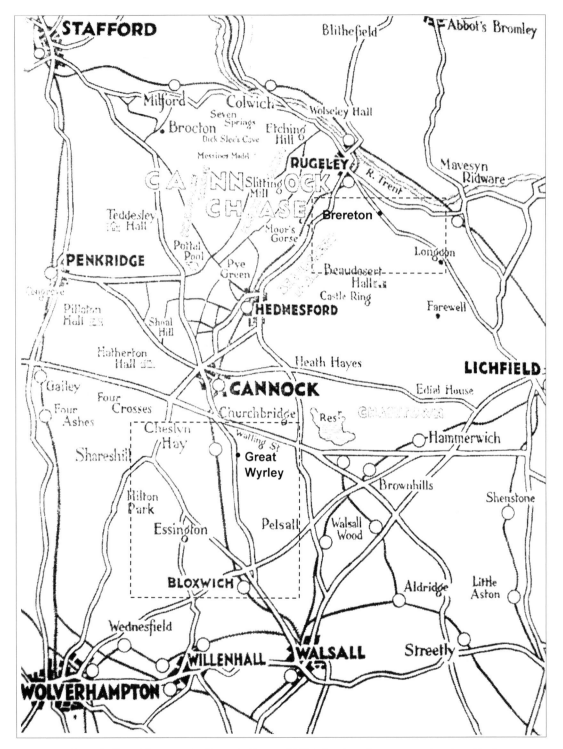

23   *Cannock Chase. Mining on the Cannock Chase coalfield before the 19th century was largely confined to Beaudesert Park and the area between Cannock and Bloxwich.*

24 *Part of the Earl of Dudley's colliery empire graphically portrayed c.1850.*

a year and numbers employed approached ten thousand. But for the many small pits working South Staffordshire's accessible seams, where horse gins continued winding coal into the 1920s, easy winnings were a disincentive to modernisation. Steam haulage had been introduced at William Gilpin's mine at Colepit Field near Great Wyrley, leased to supply Gilpin's edge tool business, by 1800. Capital investment and long-term planning was now flowing into the deeper, more progressive pits of Cannock Chase and North Staffordshire. Here the industry was set to boom.

After voluntary liquidation in 1887, it took the New British Iron Company (itself born out of the financial wreckage of an earlier British Iron Company in the 1840s) the best part of a decade to find a buyer in Shelah Garratt and Son, for New Hawne, Timbertree and the other collieries that had supplied their Corngreaves Ironworks, despite the fact they were among the best equipped and most productive pits in the Black Country. Millions of tons of coal lay under water in South Staffordshire. Much of the iron ore was played out. Continued activity in the south of the county depended on successful drainage operations and penetration of the deep, concealed measures.

2

The Cost of Winning

Coal is prone to spontaneous combustion and coal dust suspended in a gaseous atmosphere is extremely volatile. Fire, along with rock falls, ventilation and drainage, were constant problems as the depth of mines increased. Spreading powdered shale and limestone helped suppress coal dust. Circulating fresh air through twin shafts linked to the header tunnel provided simple ventilation. Temperature differences at the surface created a rudimentary draw on the convection principle that hot air rises. Natural processes were encouraged by using water to cool the air in a downcast shaft and by careful use of fire in an upcast shaft. The earliest documented instance of heat being used in this way is at Cheadle in the mid-17th century, when a fire basket was lowered into the upcast. Furnaces located at the bottom of upcast shafts came into use later. As coal faces extended away from the gateway or main underground

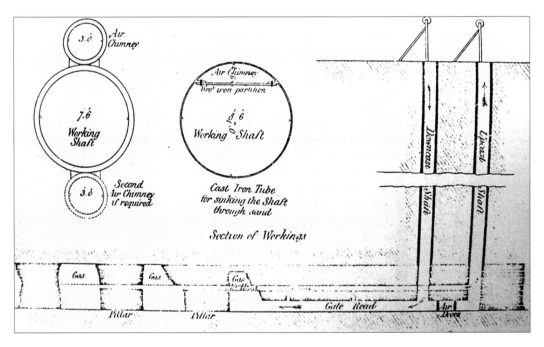

25 *Application of convection principles to mine ventilation, from the proceedings of the Institute of Mining Engineers, 1815.*

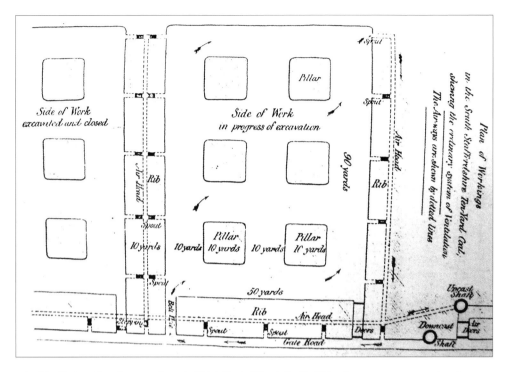

26 *Ventilation of roadways cut into the Thick Coal of South Staffordshire, from a paper presented to the Institute of Mining Engineers in 1815.*

road, doors were used to direct the flow of air. Close to the face these were temporary, makeshift affairs made of sackcloth.

Various gases encountered were known collectively as 'damp'. Common hazards were carbon dioxide or 'choke damp' and a range of inflammable gases, chiefly methane, commonly referred to as 'firedamp'. Candles provided rudimentary lighting. Naked lights and combustible gases make a dangerous combination but a blue halo or cap above the flame gave an early indication of the presence of methane and sudden snuffing was a useful warning of high levels of carbon dioxide. An antidote to choke damp described by Robert Plot in 1686 involved bringing affected miners to the surface and to:

> Dig a hole in the ground, and lay them flat on their belleys with their faces in

the hole, which (if not too far gone) infallibly recovers them.

Flint and steel mills invented in the 1730s by Carlisle Spedding gave a continuous stream of sparks when a wheel was rotated. These were marginally safer than a naked flame, but the mills were cumbersome in operation and needed frequent adjustment to compensate for flints being worn down by constant abrasion. By the time Sir Humphry Davy's safety lamp became available in 1815, a year after its invention, James Ryan, dubbed 'Hellfire Jack', had shown how to overcome the persistent problem caused by explosive gases collecting in concentrated pockets in the Thick Coal by driving ventilation headers through upper strata. Despite technical progress, accidents continued.

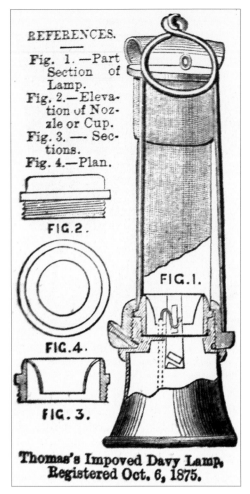

REFERENCES.

Fig. 1.—Part Section of Lamp.
Fig. 2.—Elevation of Nozzle or Cup.
Fig. 3. —. Sections.
Fig. 4.—Plan.

FIG.2.

FIG.4.

FIG.1.

FIG.3.

Thomas's Impoved Davy Lamp, Registered Oct. 6, 1875.

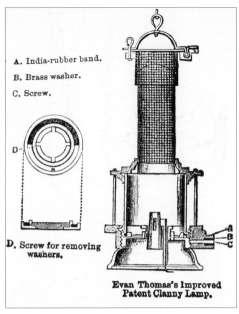

A. India-rubber band.
B. Brass washer.
C. Screw.
D. Screw for removing washers.

Evan Thomas's Improved Patent Clanny Lamp.

28 (above) *Thomas's improved Clanny lamp, 1875. The safety lamp patented by Dr William Clanny had a shorter gauze funnel than the Davy lamp and a glass cylinder that gave slightly increased illumination.*

27 (left) *Evan Thomas's improved Davy lamp, 1875. Sir Humphry Davy's safety lamp of 1814 used a protective gauze mesh to prevent the naked flame within from causing an explosion. Various adaptations and enhancements of Davy's basic design followed.*

Davy's was one of three safety lamps that appeared at much the same time. Dr William Clanny and George Stephenson both produced similar models. Each of these early designs used a gauze mesh funnel to shield the flame, based on the principle that an explosion was unable to pass through the membrane and would be contained within the lamp. They were unsafe in strong air currents and gave poor illumination. The Clanny lamp, with a shorter length of gauze set above a glass cylinder, was the brightest but still gave off less light than a naked flame candle. Tallow or oil was used to fuel the flame. Using two or more gauzes and, in designs such as the Mueseler oil lamp, a metal chimney to act as a combustion tube and prevent smoke mixing with inlet air, improved functional performance; the addition of reflectors boosted lighting. Before these developments, it was common for miners to remove the top of the lamp for better illumination, in the process exposing the flame and nullifying the safety aspect. Lamps were locked or riveted in an attempt to prevent the practice. Most collieries had regulations restricting those authorised to expose a naked flame underground to the firemen responsible for removing concentrations of gas by controlled explosion, and to those in charge of shot

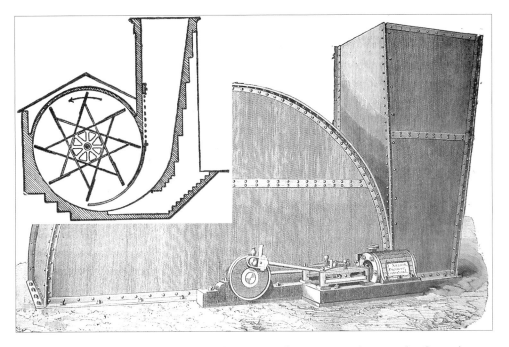

29 *Guibal fan, the first successful centrifugal design. Invented in 1862, it greatly improved airflow under ground. Eight rectangular blades were attached to an octagonal hub. Output was regulated by a shutter mechanism. Both single- and double-inlet types were produced.*

blasting operations. There were also rules banning smoking. But lamps returned at the end of a stint often showed signs of tampering and false keys circulated widely. As a control, numbered 'checks' or 'tallies' were exchanged for a lamp at the start of a shift and given back when the lamp was returned to the lamp room.

In 1862 it became a minimum legal requirement for mines to have at least two ventilation shafts. Fans were introduced for circulating air in the roadways. There were two basic types of fan, those using centrifugal principles and simpler propeller varieties. The first successful centrifugal design, the Guibal fan, was invented in 1862. By the 1870s it was widely used and greatly improved airflow underground. A Guibal fan, 40 feet in diameter and 12 feet wide, installed at Cannock Wood Colliery was capable of drawing up to 204,000 cubic feet of stale air from below ground per minute. Later refinements included

the Waddle fan, with 24 alternately long and short backward curving blades, the fully enclosed multi-vaned 'indestructible' Walker fan, and the popular Capell fan, among others. Importantly, advances led to fans that could be reversed in an emergency, for example in the case of fire in the downcast shaft or intake airways.

Early steam driven fans were gradually converted to electrical operation. Where the contours of the land allowed sufficient fall to drain floodwater by gravity, soughs or gutters were dug. When that option was not available the alternative was to use a manual pump or horse-powered gin to raise water by the barrel load for disposal in a reservoir dug for the purpose.

Simple suction pumps, using a tight fitting piston in a cylinder to create a vacuum, became available in the 16th century but were constrained by atmospheric pressure to raising water little more than 30 feet at a time. Thomas Savery, an army officer from Cornwall who had witnessed the limitations of these pumps in his local tin mines, patented an engine in 1698 using steam pressure to augment performance that he called 'The Miners' Friend'. In 1706 one of Savery's engines was installed in an attempt to save Broad Water Colliery, Wednesbury. It was not up to the job and the mines were lost. In the words of a contemporary account:

> The engine here erected could not be brought to answer the end proposed; for the body of water being so great, such a quantity was to be raised, and so large a fire required, as rent the whole machine to pieces, so that after the loss of much time, labour and money, Mr Savery was forced to give up the work, and so the engine was laid aside as useless, and the scheme for raising water was dropt as impracticable.

Thomas Newcomen of Dartmouth (1663-1729) supplied the technological leap that made atmospheric or 'fire engines' powered by steam a practical proposition. Savery condensed steam in a tank to produce a vacuum that drew down a tight-fitting piston in a cylinder. Newcomen created a vacuum inside the cylinder itself. A balanced crossbeam coupled to rods transferred power to a pump at the foot of the pit shaft. The beam was raised as the piston was drawn down. At the end of the stroke, the weight of the mechanism returned the piston to the top of a vertical open-topped cylinder. Newcomen's invention was capable of performing up to 12 cycles per minute, each stroke raising ten gallons of water and pumping it to heights of 150 feet, the equivalent of five and a half horsepower. In 1712 the very first Newcomen engine to be installed anywhere in the world was assembled at the Coneygre Colliery

of Lord Dudley and Ward, near Tipton, probably on the site now occupied by the Black Country Museum. It attracted considerable attention as one witness, a Swedish national, reported:

> Many who were anxious to make use of this invention in their mines and to acquire the necessary knowledge for constructing a similar wonderful machine, came from all parts of England and abroad to Dudley Castle.

Among those keen to learn more was the Spanish Ambassador. He was disappointed. The same account records:

> [He] was not allowed to enter the engine house in spite of big rewards, but had to return to London in a bad temper without having had a chance to see more than the wonderful effect, which this small machine was able to produce.

Working within the terms of Savery's patent enabled Newcomen to exploit his engine to the full by limiting application of his ideas. Once the patent expired, others drew on the design to manufacture similar machines. In 1756 Staffordshire-born engineer James Brindley, better known today as the great pioneer of England's canal system, built an engine for Thomas Broad at Fenton. Newcomen's single-stroke engine was effective but alternately heating and cooling the cylinder with each stroke of the piston wasted power. Large quantities of coal were consumed firing the boiler.

James Watt noted the problems at first hand when undertaking repairs. By closing the cylinder and adding a separate condensation tank that allowed the cylinder to remain heated, Watt developed the first genuine steam engine. It was economical in use and became the industry standard

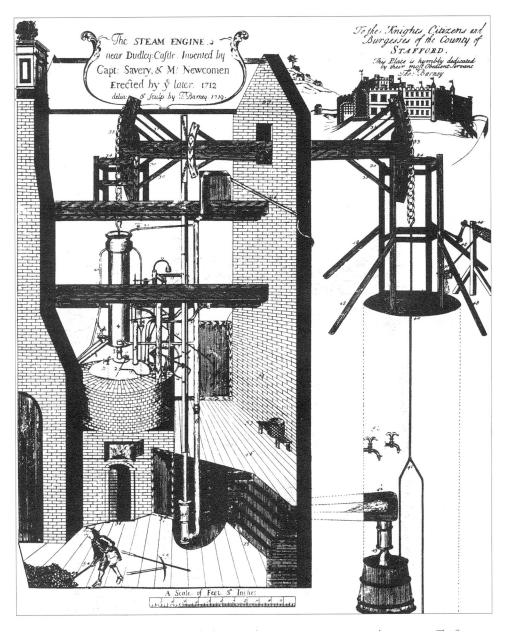

30 *Thomas Newcomen's innovations made the atmospheric steam engine a practical proposition. The first op-erational Newcomen engine was installed at Coneygre Colliery near Tipton in 1712. Condensing steam produced a vacuum, forcing a tight-fitting piston into an open-topped cylinder to create a stroke of the engine and rock the connected beam.*

for a century. The first large-scale engine of any size incorporating Watt's ground-breaking principles was built by Matthew Boulton and installed at Bentley, Banner and Company's Bloomfield Colliery, Dudley in 1776. Named the 'Parliament Engine', it boasted a 50 inch bore and had a stroke of seven feet. *Aris's Birmingham Gazette* carried the story of the machine's impressive debut:

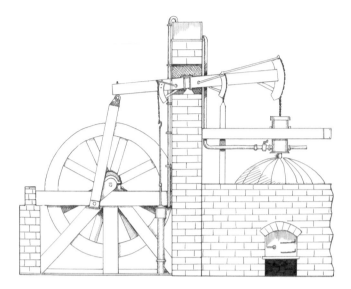

31 (left) *Thomas Newcomen atmospheric engine fitted with a crank and flywheel. Originally used for pumping water, Newcomen-style engines were soon adapted for winding.*

32 (opposite) *High pressure condensing steam pumping engine by F. & J. Silvester, with 100in. bore and 12ft stroke, used for mines drainage from the mid-19th century.*

From the first moment of its setting to work, it made about 14 to 15 strokes per minute, and emptied the engine pit [90 feet deep and two-thirds full of water] in less than an hour.

Engines were soon adapted for winding coal and manriding. Touring England to witness the industrial transformation underway in 1785, the La Rochefoucauld brothers visited John Wilkinson's Bilston colliery and noted

> two shafts going down into one of Mr Wilkinson's coal mines; it is nearly 300ft down, and here the same steam-pump that lowers and raises the buckets full of coal also extracts all the water in the mine – a double operation that makes a great saving.

A Newcomen-style engine built around 1830 was still in use at Windmill End Colliery in 1930 when it was purchased by the Henry Ford Museum and shipped across the Atlantic to be put on display at Bearborn, Michigan.

In the mid-18th century the more easily exploited coalfield of South Staffordshire was producing twice as much coal as the rest of the county combined. Motivated by short-term profits, what remained of the shallow seams was plundered over the next century without much thought about wasteful practices or conserving future stocks. Drainage was a major problem. So many shafts had been sunk in a profligate scramble for easy winnings in the most productive areas that subsidence affected natural drainage. Mines that ceased working were rarely decommissioned effectively. In 1750 Thomas Tomkye and Burslem Sparrow were among the most prominent of a number of local coalmasters found guilty at Wednesbury Manor Court of failing to close mines properly. Ordered to take action or face fines, they chose to pay the fines according to records of later proceedings.

Floodwater trapped in abandoned diggings was a constant threat to new projects. A partnership formed in 1677 between Lord Dudley and Ward and John Grey, Lord of Enville to work together on draining pits in Amblecote and

Kingswinford had set an early, but all too rare, example of what was needed.

In 1854 Tipton's larger colliery owners agreed in principle to a jointly funded co-operative pumping effort. In the event, there were simply too many people involved and the potential costs too high for voluntary concerted action. Those who took part in the scheme objected to paying for draining the non-contributing mines. There were also practical problems. With no alternative method of dispersal, floodwater pumped to the surface was fed into local waterways from where some inevitably seeped back underground.

Over the life of the Earl of Dudley's Saltwells Colliery (named from a brine well that fed a bath house), in that part of the South Staffordshire coalfield extending between Cradley Heath and Netherton in Worcestershire, around thirty separate pits were sunk. The colliery was centrally drained from a pumping engine at No. 20 Pit. In each of the other pits a 30ft rib of coal was left, forming a two-mile barrier around the site to prevent flooding.

In the early 1870s West Bromwich Colliery Company was formed specifically

to drain and re-open Great Bridge Colliery and Brickhouse Colliery, two potentially productive mines closed by flooding. Such ventures were the exception. In overall terms, little was done to make accessible an estimated 150 million tons of submerged coal. Matters were taken out of local hands by the passing of the South Staffordshire Mines Drainage Act in 1873. Under the terms of the Act, a Commission with authority to raise a levy was set up. A Parliamentary Review carried out in 1920 summed up the state of affairs inherited by the Drainage Commission and the results of their early efforts:

> Extensive mining of the most elementary character, vigorously prosecuted for centuries, with no regard to the damage done to the surface or contiguous streams, has caused a large part of the coalfield at the present time to resemble nothing so much as a waterlogged rabbit warren … Mining has been left to a great extent in the hands of men with diverse interests and small capital, who have been either unwilling or unable to efficiently combine to fight the incursion of the water into the mines … One of the first duties performed by the newly elected Commissioners was to embank and make watertight the main streams over the broken ground. This involved a heavy but justifiable expenditure, and in 1882 it was considered that a great improvement had been effected and that the quantity of water entering the mines had been reduced by one-half.

Initially the drainage tariff was set at one penny on each ton of coal raised. Charges also covered ironstone, fireclay and other minerals. Wrangling over liabilities hindered progress. An independent arbitration committee, with a Queen's Counsel and a professional mining engineer

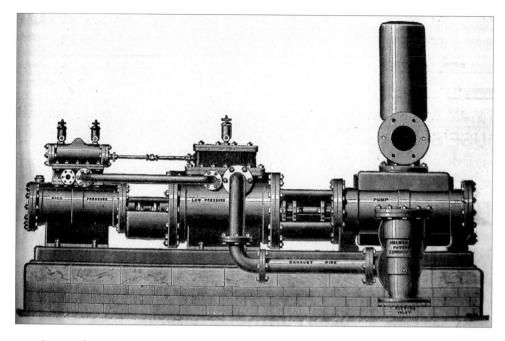

33 *Compound steam pumping engine typical of the kind in use in South Staffordshire after the passing of the Mines Drainage Act in 1873.*

among the members, was appointed to set the amount to be levied. Mine owners in Oldbury successfully lobbied to be excluded from the Drainage Act on the grounds that water from Oldbury was contained and did not drain outside the local area. When the Commissioners applied for an extension to their powers of enforcement in 1878, Bilston fought for a similar clause, claiming:

> The Commissioners would cram the threatened rates down the throats of the Bilston people if the Bilston people did not do what the Oldbury people had done – shown a bold front.

Bilston's case was that while they accepted water discharged from mines in their area created problems elsewhere and particularly in Tipton, they argued it was only a result of 'the hollows which the Tipton mine owners have got rich by making'.

Despite considerable localised opposition, the Drainage Commission pressed forward with an ambitious programme. Pumping operations were accompanied by improvements to surface drainage. Watercourses were straightened, and porous channels given puddled clay linings. Much was achieved but the cost was high. In 1886 the levy on coal was raised to nine pence per ton. Within months the iron industry experienced one of its cyclical downturns with knock-on effects for the price of coal. Some mines closed to avoid paying the drainage levy. Chairman of Commissioners Richard Williams, already facing censure over expenditure, had a request for additional powers and increased funding turned down and resigned in 1888.

Pumping operations continued but the impetus was lost. The scale of the problem was illustrated by the Parliamentary

34 *Women coal sorters in the Black Country in the early 20th century. Few women worked at Staffordshire pits.*

Enquiry of 1920 that estimated 40 tons of water drained for every ton of coal won. A decision was taken to abandon pumping at Tipton, the worst affected area. With depressed prices, over-production and the introduction of quotas, there was a gradual winding down of drainage operations across South Staffordshire.

Although women and girls loaded coal barges, it was unusual to find women employed in Staffordshire's pits. The Mines Act of 1842 restricted women to surface operations only and a few 'pit bank wenches' worked as coal pickers and sorters in the Black Country. Boys as young as seven worked up to 12 hour shifts underground in the collieries of South Staffordshire before the same legislation raised the legal minimum to 10 years of age from 1 March 1843. The Act was not without opposition. Urging his fellow peers in the House of Lords to reject the Bill, Lord Londonderry declared:

Here is a Bill which will prevent a strapping young fellow from following his father into one of my coal mines at whatever age he chooses. Here is a Bill which will prevent this fine young fellow from pursuing a very harmless occupation.

Orphans and pauper children dependent on parish charity were often compulsorily apprenticed to earn their keep. In the mines of North Staffordshire boys were generally aged 12 and over. Apprentices were fed, clothed and given lodging by the butty to whom they were indentured but received no pay, only pocket money until they finished their term at age 21. A report to the Commission on the Employment of Children that paved the way for the 1842 Mines Act drew a parallel with slavery in the colonies that had ended a decade earlier.

Above ground, younger boys drove the gin horses. Below the surface, apprentices

35 (left) *Acme 'snap' tin with handle enabling it to be fastened to a belt. Plastic water bottles replaced tin 'clock' containers.*

36 (right) *Circular tin water bottles called 'clocks' were taken underground.*

usually began as door boys or 'trappers', opening and closing ventilation doors to allow horse-drivers and tubs through. Others swept rails as 'way-cleaners', acted as 'putter boys' loading coal, or worked as 'hurriers' pushing tubs, corves and sledges from the stall gates to the roadway. Where tunnels were too narrow to allow haulage by ponies, for example in the Cheadle pits where the 'Woodhead', 'Standing' and 'Littley' seams were rarely much more than three feet deep, children might be employed to pull tubs by means of a leather shoulder harness known as a 'byatt' or 'dog belt'. Boys cleaned out the 'hole' after coal had been removed and filled baskets with slack. Many went on to loading skips, horse driving and facework. The working week for children was capped at 54 hours in 1887 when the age limit for working both above and below ground was raised to twelve. The usual arguments were employed against increasing the age limit: 'the boys were healthy' and they 'enjoyed their work'; 'mines would be uneconomic without them'; and 'those arguing for the age to be raised were being sentimental'. The age limit was raised to 13 in 1900, and

increased again to 14 by the Coal Mines Act of 1911. In 1937 legislation was passed restricting under-18s to daylight shifts only.

Conditions underground were grim. Gnats, locally 'midgins', thrived in the heat and humidity. Rats and mice brought in accidentally with horse feed and hay bales bred and multiplied. Life expectancy for miners in the 19th century was 10 years below the national average. A packed lunch or 'snap' was taken underground in tin containers fitted with handles that enabled them to be looped onto a belt. Water bottles, also made of tin, were known as 'clocks' from their circular shape. Standard miners' dress was flat cap, flannel shirt, waistcoat, moleskin trousers and either boots or clogs. At the coalface men frequently worked naked to the waist. Coal dust clotting in open cuts healed to leave livid blue scars, marks of an unnatural blood brotherhood between man and material. Particularly in South Staffordshire, trousers were generally tied with 'yorks' or 'yocks' below the knees to prevent the bottoms dragging in the mud (or stop rats running up their legs as some liked to claim!).

37 *Miners working the Thick Coal in South Staffordshire, c.1900. Men frequently worked naked to the waist in the humid conditions at the coalface. Before safety helmets were introduced in the 1930s, standard headgear was a flat cap.*

38 *Snap time in Bottom Deep seam, Old Coppice (Hawkins) Colliery, 1915. The miners are, left to right: Tom Smith (fireman), George Horney, Frank Sibborn, Cyril Dickenson, Frank Hunt, Matt Hennegan. In the foreground is Tom Smith junior.*

A shift was defined as a 'stint', a flexible period of time defined by how long it took to dig a set amount, commonly around three cubic yards, of coal. Fit, robust miners might complete as many as two-and-a-half stints in a working day. Colliers were hired for short periods, sometimes as day workers, but more usually for one or two weeks at a time. 'Steady work' was not a feature of the industry. Earnings varied, fluctuating with the price of coal. A foreman or 'doggy' was paid extra to enforce discipline underground. Insecurity of employment meant any dispute about safety or reluctance to follow orders was likely to result in instant dismissal and difficulty in finding alternative work in the area. One collier summed up the situation when giving evidence before the Midland Mining Commission in 1843:

> If you know there is danger and say you won't go, the butty will say 'then you must go up, and there's no more work for you'.

Butties found support for a tough approach in the courts. In 1861, after entering into an agreement for 14 days work but refusing to start when he discovered water in the pit, collier Thomas Garrington was sentenced by Wednesbury Magistrates to three weeks' hard labour.

There were lean times but colliers were generally among the best paid workers. Many began as pit boys, learning the business inside out as they worked their way up, often following in the footsteps of fathers and grandfathers. Despite the hardships and a lack of training that put lives at risk, the mines also attracted inexperienced men eager for work and higher wages than could be earned as an agricultural labourer or domestic servant. An estimated 5,000 miners in Staffordshire at the close of the 17th century had risen to more than 25,000 by the 1850s. Parting miners from their hard-earned wages became part and parcel of the butty system. Charter masters frequently paid workers in goods, a custom known as 'truck' or 'tommy'. Holding back a week's pay in hand with a fortnightly 'reckoning' forced workers to shop with them using credit tickets. Beer shops were set up to supply miners with a daily allowance of ale at the pithead. A penny a day was deducted from earnings of around 2s. 6d. for a quart of beer. Many butties brewed their own ale; others had a financial stake in local public houses. Weekend binges became a way of life for many miners. Bilston doctor Francis Palmer testified to the beer house entertainment enjoyed by colliers that frequently involved a type of clog dance called the double shuffle:

> The noise of the shoes is the source of delight in this dance, and the hobnails of the colliers afford great advantage. Sometimes in summer they will sit all around the door of the public house in a great circle, all on their haunches, and every man his bulldog between his knees, and in this position they drink and smoke.

Monday following fortnightly payday became a customary miners' 'holiday', an unauthorised but accepted part of working practices to allow recovery from the excesses of the previous two days. In his 1840 report on child labour in the Potteries to the House of Commons Commission of Enquiry, Samuel Scriven wrote:

> Colliers, who employ young children to assist in their labours, are a deformed, sickly class; here, as elsewhere, subject to fits of great intemperance,

adding of the working class generally:

39 *Miners' clogs. Soles were either protected with hobnails or fitted with horseshoe-style iron rims.*

conditions first-hand and interviewed some of those employed. It proved to be an eye-opening experience. After visiting Kidsgrove, he reported:

> Of all the occupations of life this to me appears the most laborious, dismal, and dangerous. To be deprived of the light of Heaven six days in the week, of all social intercourse with friends, and of every domestic happiness, and yet be satisfied, and choose it in preference to any other, is indeed extraordinary: but so it is. Ask them and 19 out of 20 will say, 'I'd rather be collier than farmer or potter'.

Intemperance in intoxicating drink is a serious evil. Many of them allowing their families almost to starve in order that they may indulge in this vice. The numbers of public houses, beer, and spirit shops being great, and the latter appearing to enjoy a very prosperous trade.

Truck schemes operated in other industries and areas but nowhere as extensively as in the Staffordshire coalfields. Not all truck customs were exploitative. Properly run schemes, for example those operated by Quaker iron and coalmaster Samuel Lloyd, ensured decent quality goods at low prices. Taking evidence from Thomas Kinnersley's agent at Kidsgrove, Scriven observed:

> It is always the practice to pay them in hard cash or bank notes; if there is an exception to this, it is to sell them, at something less than the market price, a strike of wheat, and grind it for them in the bargain. This is an accommodation for them; it is done at their own request. They can buy flour if they like elsewhere, but it would be at a higher price and of inferior quality.

Scriven visited mines throughout North Staffordshire as well as two collieries on the Cannock Chase field. He witnessed

Fatalities resulting from accidents were all too frequent. Roof falls accounted for most incidents. Parish registers in mining districts make grim reading. Work stopped when there was a death. All colliers attended a colleague's funeral with the butty generally supplying refreshments. Coroners made use of local public houses. The *Rose and Crown*, Willenhall, *Barrel Inn*, Bilston, and *Red Lion*, Brereton all hosted inquests in 1861. Compensation liabilities for death or injury sustained by workers usually formed part of individual charters. Owners, butties and miners collectively contributed to sick pay and widows' allowances. Miners usually paid an agreed levy whenever there was a serious incident. Accident accounts were patchy before the Mines Act of 1842 introduced more consistent recording.

In June 1843 an explosion at Broadfield Colliery's Ash Pit, Goldenhill killed nine. Eleven died in an explosion at Five Ways Colliery, Rowley Regis in October 1844. In 1846 there were fatalities at: Fire Clay Pit, Deepfields Colliery, Bilston (five dead); Sladderhill Colliery, Audley, where a naked flame ignited a pocket of gas (two dead); and at Round's Green Colliery, Oldbury, considered a low-risk pit where candles

40 (left) *Shaft top with the cage ready to be lowered at North Staffordshire Coal and Iron Company's No. 1 'Big Banbury' Pit, Talke, scene of a massive explosion in 1866.*

41 (right) *The Swan Inn, Talke hosted an inquiry into the explosion at Big Banbury Pit that killed 91 miners in 1866. Coroners frequently made use of rooms in local public houses to investigate accidents.*

were still routinely used underground (19 dead). Five miners died in an explosion at Yew Tree Colliery, Rowley Regis in 1847, and 12 at Heathfield Colliery, Darlaston in 1848. A blast at Great Bridge Colliery, Dudley in 1849, allegedly caused by the doggy unscrewing his lamp, resulted in 14 miners losing their lives. Explosions rocked Wigglesworth Colliery, Sedgley in 1850 (five dead); White Hill Colliery, Kidsgrove in 1851 (nine dead); Ramrod Hall, Oldbury in 1856 (11 dead); and Cleveland Colliery, Tipton in 1862 (seven dead).

Four men were trapped at Steer's Meadow Colliery, Wednesbury in 1863 when Lea Brook burst its banks as a result of subsidence caused by an underground fire in sealed off workings. A mill downstream opened its sluices to bring down water levels. After a 30-hour rescue effort hampered by both fire and flood a sole survivor emerged.

An accident in 1866 at the North Staffordshire Coal and Iron Company's No. 1 or 'Big Banbury' Pit was the start of a disastrous decade at Talke. Ninety-one died in a massive explosion. North Staffordshire Railway ran special trains for 'sympathisers

and sightseers'. A coroner's inquiry held locally at the *Swan Inn* heard a catalogue of evidence pointing to lax discipline, including smoking of pipes underground. Safety lamps at the mine were fitted with locks but 27 keys were found on rescued miners. A fund set up to provide financial assistance to dependants of victims grew into the North Staffordshire Permanent Relief Society. Seven years later, when an explosion triggered by shot-blasting killed 18 men in the same Big Banbury Pit in 1873, only 23 of the workforce of three hundred had joined the Relief Society, and just three of those who died were members. A similar shot-firing incident at Talke, this time at Bunker's Hill Colliery, cost 43 lives in 1875.

A hissing cloud of escaping steam in the early hours of 17 March 1869 at the Earl of Dudley's No. 29 Pit, Wallows Colliery, Brierley Hill, commonly known as 'Nine Locks', signalled the extinguishing of the ventilation furnace at the foot of the upcast. When banksman Joseph Lewis and doggy Samuel Thompson were lowered in the cage to investigate they found the shaft half full of water. Thirteen men on the nightshift were trapped below

42 *People gathering around the pithead and engine house of Talke Colliery after a disastrous explosion in 1873. This engraving was produced for a special* Illustrated London News *supplement.*

43 *The Stoke* Sentinel *marked the Diglake Colliery flood disaster of 1895 with a special supplement. Pictured (below, left to right) are members of the rescue party: Joseph Bateman, John Boulton, John Watts, William Dodd, John Carter, Amos Hinkley. Under manager William Dodd won the Albert Medal for his bravery in leading the rescue. Other members of the team received Royal Humane Society awards.*

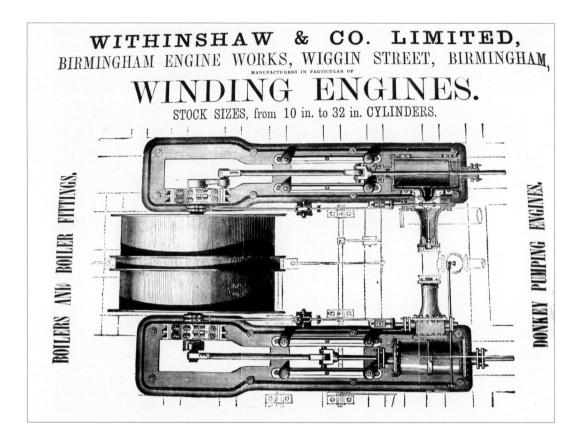

ground. Because they were not working in the deepest part of the pit there was initial optimism that they were alive. An additional pumping engine was brought in and a large bucket lowered and raised manually in a desperate race against time. Families kept vigil at the pithead for four days, but when rescuers eventually reached the foot of the shaft they discovered heavy concentrations of carbon dioxide and calls met with silence. On the following day, as the ongoing operation began to be scaled down, faint sounds were heard. Volunteers descended and with the aid of a raft began to bring out the trapped men. Miraculously only one life was lost in the ordeal. Vigorous pumping activity had helped air to circulate and dispersed the worst of the gases. The men had survived by chewing coal and boot leather but

clearly understood the seriousness of their plight and were resigned to the worst. Before their lights failed, last letters had been written to families and loved ones.

Explosions killed 19 at Silverdale Colliery's Sheriff Pit, Newcastle in 1870, and 17 at Bignall Hill Colliery, Audley in 1874. On 14 November 1872, 21 died at Pelsall Hall Colliery, Walsall when cutting breached an old gate road filled with floodwater. At the inquest, held in the *Station Inn*, the mine surveyor confirmed that, although no old workings were recorded on the site, he had spoken to an older resident who recalled being told of shafts in the area. In 1895 floodwater that had collected in old workings nearby broke through at Diglake Colliery, Audley drowning 77.

Gunpowder was in widespread use for shot-blasting. Nitro-glycerine was

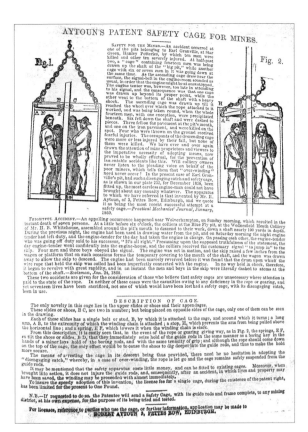

44 (opposite) *Withinshaw winding engine, one of a range of locally made engines available to Staffordshire collieries in the 1870s.*

45 (right) *Robert Aytoun patent safety cage. A series of overwinding accidents in the late 19th century led to the development of safety mechanisms to prevent cages being wound into the headgear.*

dangerously unstable in low temperatures and in the form of dynamite it was unreliable in damp conditions. Three separate explosions caused by shot-firing at Apedale Colliery, Newcastle in 1878, 1885 and 1891 resulted in 42 deaths. A further 62 fatalities at Madeley and Leycett Colliery in 1880 were followed by eight deaths at Great Fenton in 1885. An underground smithy ignited coal dust at Whitfield Colliery, Tunstall in 1881 killing 21. The deaths of seven miners in an explosion at Hall End Colliery, West Bromwich in 1884 were attributed to someone striking a match. Spontaneous combustion detonated a massive explosion at Mossfield Colliery, Longton in 1889, resulting in 64 dead.

Overall mine safety and productivity relied on the winding engine. Pit bells gave simple, clear signals: one ring 'raise'; two

rings 'lower'; and three rings 'manriding'. Power winding added the potential dangers of engine breakdown, brake failure or overwinding. Member of Parliament for Stafford and President of the National Miners' Union Alexander MacDonald, chairing a conference at Birmingham in March 1878, recalled frequent accidents including the recent deaths of two men and injuries to several others at Apedale, when the cage was wound over the pulley. Safety mechanisms that incorporated detaching hooks to shear haulage ropes and secure cages were patented by a number of engineering companies, Robert Aytoun, E.O. Ormerod and Barker Davies among the more prominent, and designed to prevent platforms being wound into the headgear. Conference delegates agreed to send a deputation to the Home Secretary to urge compulsory introduction.

46   *Winding engine house in North Staffordshire, c.1910.*

Cages hauled on steel wire ropes operated at stomach-churning speed. Engine winders took their work seriously. John Bladon and his brother were commissioned to build the steam engine and winding gear at Littleton in 1897, when Littleton Collieries began work to re-open shafts abandoned by the Cannock and Huntington Company over a decade earlier. With the engine installed, John was offered the job of winder with his son Frank Bladon as his assistant. During a training session, Frank was asked to wind the cage down the shaft under his father's supervision. From the winder's chair, Frank opened the steam valve and set the drum in motion. When the cage was halfway down the shaft, John mused aloud, 'I wonder what the time is?' Pulling a brand new pocket watch, of which he was very proud, from his waistcoat pocket, Frank replied, 'Ten minutes to two.' After

bringing the cage smoothly to a halt at the bottom of the shaft, Frank turned to his father and asked expectantly, 'How did I do, Dad?' The response was a heavy blow that sent him sprawling. 'And that is to teach you that when men's lives are at stake you never for an instant take your eyes off your engine'.

Increasingly, as the 19th century progressed, miners took out life and accident insurance. Some subscribed to friendly societies or locally organised provident and philanthropic associations, others took out policies with commercial insurance companies. The Prudential was a popular choice. Miners' associations and trade unions operated accident funds for contributing members. By the close of the 19th-century, miners' permanent relief funds were at last attracting support. One penny a week paid to a burial club ensured funeral expenses were covered.

47 *Blank inspection certificate detailing the safety checks made when testing winding engines.*

In the mid-19th century the rate of accidental death in the Staffordshire coalfield far exceeded that experienced elsewhere in the country, averaging around 160 fatalities a year from an estimated workforce of 25,000 miners. Inevitably, as mines became deeper and the numbers employed at a single pit increased, so did the scale of headline grabbing disasters. Every major occurrence resulted in a demand for 'something to be done' and often a knee-jerk government reaction. Mining legislation, almost exclusively concerned with social conditions before 1840, now began to focus on safety issues and the responsibilities of mine managers. The Coal Mines Regulation Act of 1842 included the proviso:

That it shall be lawful for one of Her Majesty's principal Secretaries of State, if

and when he shall think fit, to appoint any proper person to visit and inspect any mine or colliery.

Only 12 Inspectors, dubbed 'Blackcoats', were appointed. The government argued that too many inspectors would send the wrong message to mine owners and encourage them to believe they were absolved of liability for safety. Legislation followed in 1850, 1855 and 1860, setting a framework for mine regulation. Among the key steps taken was the requirement to notify HM Inspectorate of fatal accidents within 24 hours, and the maintenance of plans of underground workings at all collieries was made a statutory duty. Ultimate accountability remained uncertain until a legal precedent set in 1867 made clear this was not something colliery owners could delegate.

As the industry became more organised, professional engineering institutes emerged. South Staffordshire and East Worcestershire Institute of Mining Engineers, formed in 1867, had 242 members by 1876. North Staffordshire Institute of Mining Engineers was founded in 1872. On a visit to Chatterley Iron Company's Whitfield Colliery in 1874, the President of the North Staffordshire Institute was invited to cut the first turf for a new shaft to work the rich Cockshead seam, afterwards christened the Institute Shaft in honour of the occasion. Regular mines inspection, coupled with greater engineering professionalism and safer working practices, was a great step forward but mining in Staffordshire remained an inherently dangerous occupation.

Pressure from miners' associations led to the 1872 Coal Mines Regulation Act. This introduced stricter controls, requiring copies of all underground plans to be deposited centrally and making a compulsory legal requirement the employment of a manager with a certificate of competency at every colliery with a workforce in excess of 30 people. Administration of the qualification was placed under the authority of a specially established Mining Examinations Board. Other requirements included the provision of locked safety lamps, pre-shift inspections, regulations governing roof supports, specified meeting points, and rules for the withdrawal of men if danger threatened. Managers and owners faced imprisonment for wilful neglect and breaches of the law. For new sinkings, shafts had to be a minimum of 10 feet apart. From 1887 this was extended to 45 feet.

New rules governing shotfiring were introduced as electrically detonated gelatinous compounds began replacing gunpowder and fuse. From 1933 only low-freezing point explosives encased in

48 *Cambrian-style electric ignition lamp c.1880 by Thomas and Williams of Aberdare. It was fitted with a magnetic lock to inhibit tampering.*

inert protective sheathes were allowed. Importantly, the 1872 Act put an end to the worst abuses of the sub-contract system. Variations of butty arrangements known as the 'small' or 'little butty' system, subject to clearly defined and limited application, continued until the First World War. Arrangements were invariably restricted to a single section or 'stall' of a coalface.

There was never any shortage of miners willing to risk their lives for trapped colleagues, brave men with a wealth of mining experience but without any formal training and usually little in the way of specialised equipment. A Royal Commission of 1886 recommended setting up dedicated Rescue Stations. Progress was slow and inconsistent. By the 1890s many large collieries had their own ambulance teams and trained first-aiders working underground, but emergency rescue efforts still depended on volunteers.

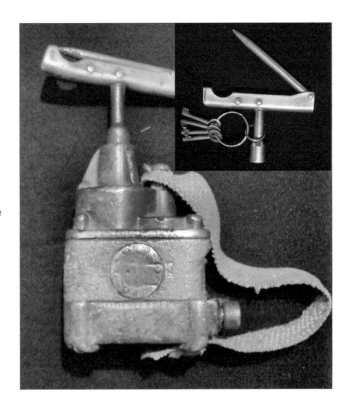

49 Little Demon *shotfiring kit. The firing key (inset) was a multi-purpose tool incorporating a 'stabber' and cartridge 'pricker'.*

50 *Hamstead Colliery, Great Barr, where a fire in 1908 killed 25 men.*

In 1904 a paper was presented to the Midland Institute of Mining Engineers urging action to create a more organised service to deal with emergencies.

A disastrous fire began in a box of candles stored near the foot of the downcast at Hamstead Colliery, Great Barr in 1908. Winding engines on the shaft were awaiting repair and the winder was on duty at the upcast. Signal wires for both shafts ran along the downcast. They were damaged when the fire started and

51 (left) *Early breathing apparatus, like this example by the Siebe-Gorman company, used hand-operated bellows positioned outside the danger area to pump fresh air along a tube to a smoke helmet.*

52 (right) *Proto mines rescue apparatus by Siebe-Gorman. The single steel cylinder contained approximately two hours supply of compressed oxygen. A pressure gauge indicated the amount remaining.*

communications with the surface severed. Specialist teams from Yorkshire, equipped with newly developed self-contained breathing apparatus, were called in to work alongside local volunteers. Twenty-five men trapped underground died, as did one of the rescuers.

Breathing apparatus involving bellows, hand-operated from outside the danger area and pumping fresh air along a tube to a helmet, had been in use for some time before Henry Fleuss patented the first practical, portable self-contained breathing apparatus in 1879. Fleuss became an advisor to the Siebe-Gorman Company and while working for them came up with the 'Proto' design that used compressed oxygen. In various

updated forms the 'Proto' remained in use, and other models such as Meco-Briggs, Gibbs and Paul followed. Brown and Mills developed an alternative liquid air system. The 'Proto' and Brown-Mills 'Aerophor' were the two types of breathing apparatus given an official stamp of approval by the Mines Rescue Research Committee of 1923. Later developments, such as the SEFA 'Sabre' liquid air equipment, were designed with a tin body that could act as an emergency sled to transport an injured miner.

Legislation introduced in 1909 required collieries to have systems in place to record exactly how many men were underground at any time. A 'two-check' system was common. Miners were issued with two

53 (left) *SEFA Sabre self-contained liquid air rescue apparatus. The tin body (later models were made of heavy duty plastic) was designed to double as a sled to carry an injured miner.*

54 (right) *Vacuum storage flask for liquid air (60 per cent oxygen and 40 per cent nitrogen). Two men using liquid air rescuers could carry a top-up supply.*

individually numbered checks or tallies, most usually of brass or zinc. One was kept on the person and the other handed to a banksman at the pithead before descending in the cage and collected at the end of the shift.

The twelve months from April 1909 to March 1910 was the worst year on record for deaths in the industry and led directly to the Coal Mines Act of 1911 that made rescue stations compulsory. Those responsible for drafting the Act had the foresight to provide for amendment by General Regulation, allowing the Act to be kept up to date without recourse to Parliament. North Staffordshire Colliery Owners' Association hit the ground

running. A temporary rescue unit issued with six sets of 'Proto' breathing equipment had been set up in a converted house in 1910 while the Bill was being debated in Parliament. The North Staffordshire station moved to permanent headquarters at Berry Hill Colliery the following year. Within a matter of months, 20 six-man brigades had been trained. Rescue brigades at Hednesford, funded by the Colliery Owners' Association of Cannock Chase, and at Trindle Road, Dudley, provided by South Staffordshire Association, were fully operational by 1918.

Specialist skills learned working with breathing apparatus in confined and often flooded conditions were called

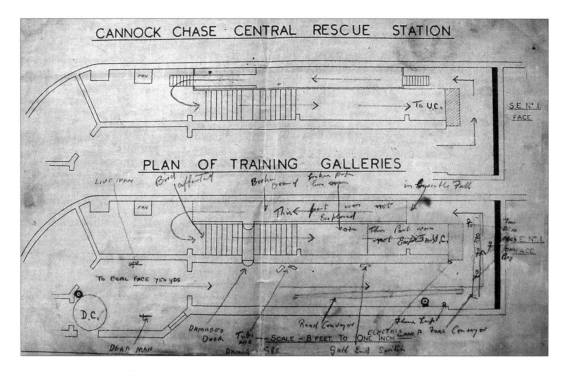

55 *Plan of Cannock Chase Rescue Station serving, showing the layout of the galleries where brigade members practised emergency rescue techniques.*

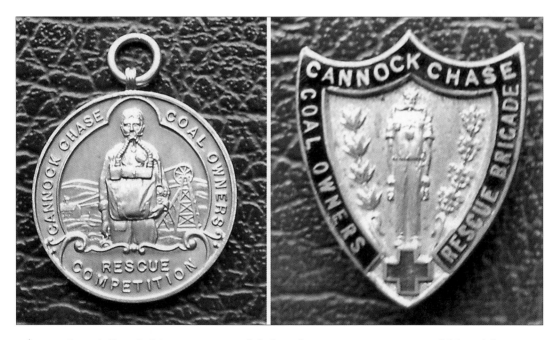

56 *Cannock Chase Coal Owners Rescue Brigade badge and rescue competition winner's medal (awarded to A. Birch in 1929). Rescue teams sharpened their skills with inter brigade contests.*

57   *Stourbridge (No. 1 Colliery) Mines Rescue Squad pictured at Beech Tree Colliery, c.1920.*

58   *The* Thetis *rescue team at Holyhead, 1939. Left to right: Tom Forsyth (Captain, Brereton Colliery), Harry Wall (Conduit Colliery), Jack Calow (West Cannock Colliery), Josh Payton (Superintendent of Hednesford Rescue Station), Les Hyden (Cannock and Rugeley Colliery), Harry Saffhill (Cannock and Leacroft Colliery), Charlie Holgate (Lieutenant, Mid Cannock Colliery).*

59   *Pit ponies rescued after 21 days trapped underground following an explosion at Jamage Pit, Bignall Hill Colliery in 1911. Six men working at the face and 27 ponies were killed in the blast.*

upon outside the mining industry. In 1939 HM submarine *Thetis* sank on its maiden voyage. Ninety-nine people were trapped on board. It was four months before the vessel was salvaged and deliberately grounded in Moelfre Bay, Anglesey. A team of men from Hednesford Rescue Station travelled to Wales to recover the bodies.

Disaster struck the Cannock Chase field in 1911 when fire near the downcast at Cannock Chase Colliery Company's No. 9 'Old Hednesford' Pit spread rapidly underground and five miners lost their lives. The same year, a gob fire set off an explosion at Jamage Pit, Bignall Hill Colliery, Audley killing six men working at the face. Twelve died in a massive blast at Hem Heath in 1915. The toll at Podmore Hall Colliery's Minnie Pit at Halmer End, Newcastle in 1918 was 155. A defective safety lamp was identified as the probable cause. At Kidsgrove, seven miners died

in at explosion at Birchenwood Colliery in 1925. A fire attributed to either a candle or an illicit cigarette killed eight at Coombs Wood in 1929. An explosion at Grove Colliery, Brownhills in 1930 killed fourteen. Six men died at West Cannock Colliery's No. 5 Pit, Hednesford in 1933, when an electrical spark from the signal bell ignited gas. Sparks from cutting machinery set off an explosion at Holditch in 1937 causing 30 deaths. A spontaneous combustion accident at Mossfield Colliery resulted in eight deaths in 1940. Unusually for New Year's Day, on 1 January 1942, most of Sneyd Colliery's miners were working normally, responding to the call for productivity in aid of the war effort. A haulage rope rubbing on the underside of a descending tub snapped under intense heat, releasing a shower of sparks that ignited coal dust. The blast travelled from the foot of No. 4 Pit along the roadway, trapping men working at two faces on the

60   *Grove Colliery, Brownhills, where 14 miners lost their lives in an explosion in 1930.*

61   *A rescued miner being tended after an explosion at West Cannock No. 5 Pit in 1933 in which six men and two horses died.*

62   *Display model of a cage signalling device invented and patented by T.H. Lund of Etchinghill, Rugeley, who worked at Brereton Colliery. It was mechanically operated by ratchet so that there was no danger of sparking and it gave both an audible and visible signal.*

63   *A group of miners from Cannock Chase at the district convalescent home, Weston-super-Mare in the 1930s.*

TO BOOT GREASING

64 *Boots were cleaned and treated with grease to repel water and keep the leather supple.*

65 *Training model of a self-rescuer offering approximately thirty minutes' protection against carbon monoxide poisoning.*

Seven-feet Banbury seam and killing fifty-seven.

The 1911 Coal Mines Act had also included provision for pithead baths and clothes drying facilities, subject to local agreements and the men meeting half the cost of maintenance. A clause in the Bill that proposed making use of the baths compulsory was removed after a debate during which one MP argued, 'You can lead a miner to water, but you can't make him bathe.' Continuing concern about the grim and unhealthy conditions in which miners worked led to further legislation. Under the terms of the Mining Industry Act of 1920, a national fund was set up, financed by a one penny per ton levy on output, for the 'social well-being, recreation and conditions of living and mining education and research'. The body created to administer the fund was initially appointed for five years but this was subsequently extended and

additional finance allocated from a royalties levy. In 1939 it evolved into the Miners' Welfare Commission. Pithead baths, canteens, social and recreational clubs, sports amenities and convalescent homes were provided from the money raised. In 1939 Hilton Main Colliery was the first on Cannock Chase to have washing facilities installed. Miners paid five pence a week to use the shower suite that also included boot cleaning and greasing facilities and two lockers, one for dirty and one for clean clothes. A canteen was serving hot meals at Mid Cannock Colliery by December 1942.

Miners were provided with dust masks carried in tin containers. After trials of various types of self-rescuer, a model by Siebe-Gorman offering approximately thirty minutes protection against carbon monoxide poisoning received official National Coal Board (NCB) approval in 1962 and became regulation issue.

66   *Lea Hall Colliery's competition-winning rescue team, 1983.*

A national Safety League was launched in 1977 with 10 divisions and a system of promotion and relegation. Wolstanton Colliery topped the league in 1979. Hem Heath, Holditch and Silverdale were all Division One stalwarts. Under the leadership of team instructor Jim Whitehouse, Lea Hall Colliery's junior and senior First Aid teams built a national reputation. Regularly representing Western Area in competitions and lifting several national titles. Staffordshire's safety record after nationalisation was second to none, and the last decade under the British Coal Corporation the safest on record.

3
Staffordshire Supreme

A singular combination of large numbers of small pits, low start-up costs, shared authority over mineral rights, accessible seams of high-quality coal, long-established tradition, and strong local demand gave rise to an employment structure and business organisation in Staffordshire distinct from anywhere else.

At the start of the 18th century teams or 'companies' of men were working up to 200 feet below the surface. Most were in business for themselves. Some as collectives worked their own pit either directly or under licence; others subcontracted their services and were paid, according to how much coal they produced, by a charter master or butty, himself subcontracted by the coal owner to oversee operations. Deep shafts, seven feet or more in width, were lined with timber shuttering reinforced with brick at weak

67 *Miners in South Staffordshire undercutting a face, a process known as 'holing out', c.1900.*

68 *Horse gin in the Dudley area, c.1900, typical of those in widespread use at small pits in South Staffordshire.*

points. Faceworkers, or 'pikemen' as the coal cutters were sometimes known from their use of picks or 'pikes', were lowered in a skip or on a platform using either a windlass or horse gin. Coal was raised by the same mechanism. Larger, more powerful 'whimsey' or more commonly 'whim' gins set away from the pit shaft and requiring a team of horses yoked abreast replaced single animal, cog and rung mechanisms. With the introduction of beam engines, steam power was used to raise skips and lower platforms simultaneously, either in tandem or in two-cage shafts. Experienced 'banksmen' directed operations above ground where unskilled labourers, hired and paid by the day, loaded waggons prior to despatch.

Various arrangements existed within the charter system for paying butties. Profit sharing appealed to some; others worked on taking a cut of an agreed price per ton paid by the mine owner, generally around 25 per cent. At the root of the system was the economic premise that the butty, invariably an experienced collier with a wealth of hard-earned practical know-how, could deliver a better return than a mine owner might expect by employing miners directly. Since capital outlay was the same for both, it is clear the margin was in raising productivity. It was the butty's job to hire a team and supply tools, blasting powder, winding equipment, carts and horses. An exception to the sub-contract team was the job of checking and verifying production at the pithead. This post was invariably held by a banksman directly accountable to the mine owner.

Butties were not wealthy capitalists. Usually they were tough, able ex-colliers whose experience and knowledge fitted them well for the task. Ventures entailed financial risk. Competition between butties squeezed already tight profit margins and, along with up-front expenditure, encouraged cost cutting. With no incentive to improve conditions or provide equipment

69 *Powder cases commonly carried five pounds of explosive.*

70 *Plan showing Staffordshire 'square work' in progress at a Dudley pit in the mid-19th century.*

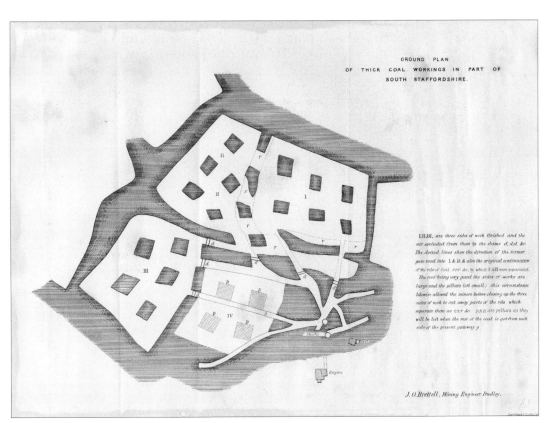

71 *Sylvester and sword used to ratchet wooden pit props into position and remove supports when retreating from a face.*

beyond the most basic, safety was often a secondary concern for butty and miner alike. Both were paid only on results and needed to produce as much coal in as short a time for as little outlay as possible.

Coal was generally dug by the method known as Staffordshire 'square work', a variant of a technique called 'bord and pillar' or sometimes 'pillar and stall'. Each miner worked individually to excavate a section of the face known as a 'stall' or 'bord'. A thick pillar of undisturbed coal was left between stalls to act as a fire rib. Working from the bottom up, a thin upright column or 'man o'war' and a horizontal beam or 'spurn' were left as supports. When the upper layers were undermined and the coal ready to fall, men o'war and spurns were cut away and the upper strata brought down in a mass, if necessary by levering from the top of the seam. Debris was packed back into the hole or 'gob', the space left when the coal was removed, to help buttress the roof. James Keir described how the various layers in the Thick Coal were worked this way in 1798:

The colliers begin to get coal by cutting a stall. This they do by cutting out the lower bed called the Humphries, the length of the stall, ten, twelve or fourteen yards; and when they have thus removed the foundation of the coal to a certain breadth, they then loosen its adhesion to the sides by cutting as high as the beds called Slipper and Sawyer, which accordingly makes the first fall of coals; the Stone-coal makes second fall; the John-coal or Sipps makes the third; the Foot-coal the fourth; the Brasil the fifth; the Benches and Tow-coal make the sixth; the Lambs make the seventh; the Jays make the eighth; the Top-slipper the ninth; and the roof is seldom cut, but only as much of it got as drops spontaneously, and can be safely collected.

Bord and pillar working was an effective though wasteful way of working the Thick Coal. The method was unsuitable for thin seams where narrow passages also made haulage difficult. Pillars were vulnerable to collapse, particularly under the pressure exerted in deep mines. By 1800, in a development known as 'panel working', underground sections of several acres were shored up by massive stone and rubble bulwarks allowing cross tunnels to be cut, a stage referred to as 'working in the whole'. As the area became worked out and faceworkers retreated, a proportion of pillars were systematically removed to increase winnings in a refinement known as 'working in the broken'.

In the mid-19th century an alternative 'longwall' technique, first practised in neighbouring Shropshire, where it was known as the 'Shropshire' or 'long-way' method, was adopted in Staffordshire for mining thinner seams. In this method, a header tunnel connected two parallel tunnels or 'gates' driven off the main haulage road. Miners worked in teams, one man lying on his side to hole under to a depth of about six feet, others to cut or blast the coal. During undercutting, short wooden 'sprags' were inserted as supports. When fully undercut, the whole face was brought down at the same time, falling into the gob for loading. The heading was advanced as a single operation, pit props moved further into the seam, and the process repeated. With the great variance experienced in the pitching and depth of the seams in North Staffordshire, both longwall and pillar and stall techniques were practised in the same mines. Hand holing was hard laborious work. Even on the Thick Coal, where faceworkers could work standing upright, or on occasion made use of ladders, the undercutter had to swing his pick lying down on his side. A popular specialist miners' tool with a spike at one end of a blade and a vertical cutting edge at the other, useful for trimming pit props, was known locally as a 'taj'.

Under the strategic leadership of the Mines Drainage Commission, radical improvements were made that extended

72   *A specialist miners' tool known locally as a 'taj'. A sharp cutting blade was used for adjusting timber shuttering and cutting out wooden pit props when retreating from a face.*

the life of the South Staffordshire coalfield into the 20th century. Under its auspices, electric pumping engines were used for the first time and technology developed that set the industry standard. Market leading businesses such as Lee Howl of Tipton, who became world famous for their pumping engines, made their name developing and supplying machinery to the Commission.

Steam-powered rotary drilling machines, invented in the 1800s by Richard Trevithick, improved the efficiency and lowered the cost of investigative boring. The first penetration of the concealed field beyond the Eastern Boundary Fault was made at Heath Colliery, West Bromwich in 1832. It was not until 1870 that Dudley mining engineer Henry Johnson, working for Lord Dartmouth, sank the first shaft into the deep reserves of South Staffordshire. His success marked the beginning of Sandwell Park Colliery and triggered further exploration including the sinking of pits at Hamstead, Great Barr. Herbert Hughes, mining engineer to the Earl of Dudley, was convinced similar

73   *Holing out by hand, with wooden pit props supporting the roof.*

74   *Baggeridge Colliery, c.1910. Baggeridge was the last working mine in South Staffordshire when it was deemed uneconomic and production ended in 1967.*

75 *Miners examining the roof at Baggeridge Colliery in the early 20th century.*

hidden reserves lay beyond the Western Fault. After initial problems led to the loss of a set of allegedly diamond-tipped bore rods (in fact a crystalline mineral diamond substitute, but still expensive) a test boring at Baggeridge Wood in 1896 hit substantial coal at 1,800 feet. It was 1910 before two shafts were completed, the second of which was so troubled by flooding a 120ft section had to be 'coffered', a technique involving three brick skins, the middle section added last and the cavity filled with concrete. A private light railway through Himley Park connected the pithead to Dawley Brook Wharf at Round Oak, and Ashwood Basin. The Great Western Railway added a mineral line later. Baggeridge Colliery, 15 years in development, marked the end of large-scale financial outlay in the South Staffordshire coalfield.

By 1840 there were around 400 collieries of varying sizes in Staffordshire employing some 28,000 men. Under the direction of the Earl of Bradford's agent, a pilot shaft was sunk into the concealed coal of the Cannock Chase field at Paul's Coppice, between Aldridge and Walsall Wood, in 1841. A test pit followed. Efforts were rewarded when measures were proved at a little over 1,700 feet, although it was not until 1874 that a lease was taken up by Alexander Brogden, William Duignam, Lauriston Lewis and Edward Peake, who with little experience but plenty of capital together formed the Walsall Wood Colliery Company in 1875. The simple furnace-fed upcast/downcast ventilation system installed proved so efficient that a fan did not replace it until the 1950s. Walsall Wood Colliery Company took over Pelsall

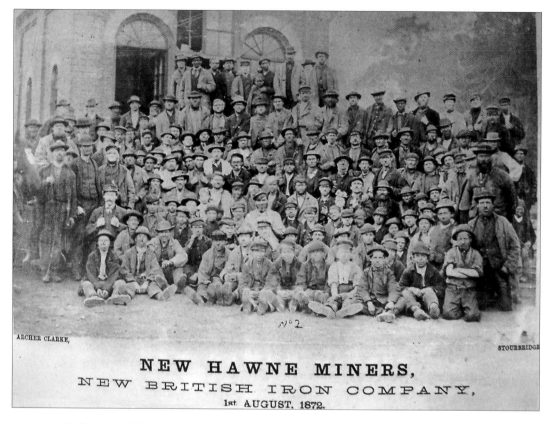

ARCHER CLARKE,

STOURBRIDGE

Nº 2

NEW HAWNE MINERS,
NEW BRITISH IRON COMPANY,
1st AUGUST, 1872.

76 *Workers gathered for a group photograph outside the winding engine house at the New British Iron Company's New Hawne Colliery, 1872.*

Colliery along with Pelsall Iron Company in the 1890s.

The first successful winning of coal from the concealed Cannock Chase coalfield had taken place in 1857 at the Coppy Hall Colliery, Aldridge operated by Reverend Bailey Williams. Production at Coppy Hall continued until 1909. Other companies were poised to take advantage of the vast deep reserves. William Harrison's Brownhills Colliery Company began sinking Grove Pit, Norton Canes in 1869. The estate of the Marquis of Anglesey had traditionally run mines under direct ownership. With family debts exceeding £1 million an injection of capital into the Paget coffers was a matter of urgency and an advertisement

was placed in the May 1853 edition of the *Mining Journal*:

Beaudesert Coal Mines – South Staffordshire
The Marquis of Anglesey will be prepared to receive offers for letting on royalty or otherwise the Collieries now at work and the unopened mines of Coal and Ironstone on Cannock Chase. On the southern portion of this property comprising an area of 3,000 acres, the following seams of coal have been proved and opened, namely:
The Yard Seam 3ft 6in about 58 yds deep
Bass Coal   6ft   about 79 yds deep
Shallow Coal 6ft 8in about 101 yds deep
Deep Coal   5ft   about 119 yds deep

The Wyrley and Essington portion of the Birmingham Canal, on which the coals are loaded, is in connection with the Hammerwich Pits, which are extensively opened and already yield 1,500 tons of coal weekly.

The advertisement went on to mention a local railway nearing completion. Hammerwich Colliery and the newly opened Uxbridge Pit near Hednesford were leased along with other land to John Robinson McLean in 1853. McClean had been chief engineer with the newly formed South Staffordshire Railway and was responsible for the Walsall to Lichfield line that ran close to the pitheads. A year after the main line opened in 1849, and with numerous branch lines under way, he had taken over the railway. McClean was a man of energy and vision. Control of the pits ensured business for his railway, and he had trained as a mining engineer at Glasgow University. Together with Hammerwich born and bred Richard Croft Chawner, he founded the Cannock Chase Colliery Company in 1854. Hammerwich became the colliery's No. 1 Pit, and Uxbridge No. 2 Pit, better known locally as the 'Fly'. A company railway was built to link the pitheads to the canal wharf and by 1858 to the main rail network. By 1870, when the company added the shallow workings and ironstone quarry of Hednesford Colliery, it had 10 operational mines. A beam engine built in Staffordshire in 1854 by Thornewill and Warham of Burton-on-Trent, originally for No. 1 Pit, was still serviceable in the 1950s.

Such extensive coal measures lay beneath Staffordshire that it is not surprising, given the expense of boring, some chances were taken with the odds by skimping on the evaluation stages. Fair Oak Colliery lost a fortune sinking pits into fissures that turned out to have been completely eroded by underground water. Incomplete proving by East Cannock Colliery Company failed to identify a vast fault and played a major part in forcing the company into bankruptcy and a bargain basement sale to the acquisitive Cannock Chase Colliery Company after just six short years of independence in 1880.

Cannock and Rugeley Colliery Company sank the first of their Cannock Wood Colliery's three shafts in 1866. Mid Cannock Colliery, East Cannock Colliery, West Cannock Colliery, Cannock and Huntington Colliery (from 1931 part of the Littleton Colliery Company), Nook and Wyrley Colliery, Cannock and Leacroft Colliery, Norton Cannock Coal Company, Cannock and Wimblebury Colliery, Hednesford Colliery, Brereton Colliery's Brick Kiln Pit, and Cannock and Rugeley's Valley Colliery were among the many enterprises begun, with varying success, during the 1870s. Twelve different seams at Valley Pit were distinguished as Bottom Robins, Brooch, Benches, Main Hard, Heathen, Stinking, Yard, Bass, Cinder, Shallow, Deep, and Mealy Grey. Miners travelled to work and back by a 'Paddy Train' of converted railway wagons with makeshift roofs.

Between 1860 and 1880 annual coal production from Cannock Chase rose from less than one million tons to around four million tons. Depression in the 1880s made small pits unprofitable, sapping much of the life out of coalmining in South Staffordshire. Investment in the Cannock Chase mines continued. Grove Colliery was linked directly to the main rail network by a bridge across the Cannock Extension Canal. Terraces of two-storey cottages were built to house miners from Shropshire and elsewhere, attracted by the demand for manpower. Bricks made of fireclay dug alongside coal were fired in colliery kilns to provide material for the building

boom. Hednesford and Cannock typified the pace of growth. Between 1861 and 1881 the population of Hednesford soared from 800 to over 9,000. Cannock grew from 2,500 in 1861 to more than 20,000 by 1891. Amenities struggled to keep pace. Cannock Chase Colliery Company helped shops, doctors and other services to become established. In 1865 the company built St Anne's church at Chasetown, paying the vicar's stipend and making all seats free at a time when pew rental was the norm. Employment at the Cannock Chase Colliery Company had grown to over 2,000 people by the mid-1880s.

Shortly before his death, in 1873, McClean made the inspired appointment of Arthur Sopwith, an experienced mining engineer who he persuaded to return to England from Bohemia to run Cannock Chase Colliery. Sopwith and his son, Shelford Francis Sopwith, who followed in his father's footsteps as manager of the company, maintained McClean's innovatory approach. Cannock Chase Colliery Company's No. 2 'Fly' Pit was the first in England and among the first in the

world to be lit underground by electricity, in 1883. A ventilation fan drove three Elwell Parker dynamos, made in Wolverhampton, to power carbon filament lights and produce a low intensity reddish glimmer. The system was extended, using flat wire winding rope as cable, to supply the manager's house, school, and St Anne's church, Chasetown, which became the first church in the country to have electric lighting. It is said the supply cables produced sufficient heat to make wet pavements steam. William Harrison's Brownhills Colliery followed suit and was generating electricity by 1886. The Cannock Chase Company's No. 3 Pit had its own power station by 1908 and in 1922 supplied electricity to light the streets of Chasetown, Chase Terrace and Boney Hay. A separate business, the Chasetown and District Electric Company set up to manage supplies, was later absorbed into the West Midlands Joint Electricity Authority.

In 1893 Robert Hanbury of Ilam Hall and lord of the manor at Norton gave his financial backing to launch Coppice Colliery at Heath Hayes. Hanbury was a

77 (opposite) *Winding engine house and head frame above the downcast shaft at Cannock and Leacroft Colliery, c.1920.*

78 (right) *Section from the pioneering underground electrical lighting system installed at Cannock Chase Colliery Company's No. 2 'Fly' Pit in 1883. Flat wire winding rope laid between profiled bricks was used as cable. A thick layer of pitch held the base bricks in place.*

prominent politician, serving as MP for Tamworth and holding appointments at various times as President of the Board of Trade and as Financial Secretary to the Treasury. Lady Ellen Hanbury, who cut the first turf when sinking began, was the nominal coalmaster and Coppice was popularly known as 'Fair Lady' in her honour. She took a keen interest in miners' welfare. During the prolonged strike of 1926 Lady Hanbury allowed local families to pick coal from the spoil heap and donated food for miners' families.

By the start of the 20th century, 33 modernised and mechanised operational pits on Cannock Chase were outperforming more than 276 traditional small mines in South Staffordshire. Activity around Cheadle and the modest fields of Shaffalong and Goldsitch Moss remained small-scale. Operational pits in the area in the latter half of the 19th century included Callow Hill, Cheadle Park, Common Side, Consall, Cross Flats, Delph House, Foxfield, Huntley, Ipstones, Little Above Park, Littley Dale, Park Hall, Park Mill, Well Street and Woodhead.

The most easily accessible seams were all but worked out when connection to the North Staffordshire Railway at Cresswell encouraged further investment in the 1890s, with Cheadle Colliery Company at the forefront of developments. By the early 20th century only Delph House and Foxfield were producing significant amounts of coal although another four small pits were still working in the area. When nationalisation took place in 1947, only Foxfield remained.

Driven by demand from the Cheshire saltworks, local potteries, brickworks and a rapidly growing iron industry, output in the Potteries field trebled in the years from 1856 to 1870 despite the deep-lying nature of workable seams. Mining at Apedale had reportedly reached depths of more than 2,150 feet by 1840. Throughout North Staffordshire, constant maintenance was required to keep flooding under control. When the death of owner Hugh Henshall Williamson temporarily halted pumping at Pinnox and Scotia in 1867, both pits filled with water and had to be closed. In Burslem, Sneyd Colliery, Jackfield

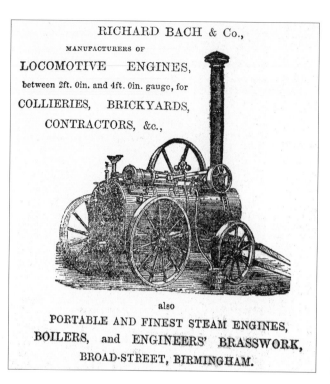

79   *Richard Bach of Birmingham supplied winding engines and locomotives to local collieries and to companies worldwide.*

80   *Sneyd Colliery between Burslem and Smallthorne, c.1910.*

Colliery, Stanfield Colliery and Bank Top Colliery had been abandoned. Under William Heath's direction in the 1880s, the saturated seams were sealed off enabling the shafts to be pumped dry and then extended to reach drier seams below.

As in South Staffordshire, it was iron manufacturers, notably William Hanbury Sparrow, who operated in both the north and south of the county; the Williamson brothers, the Heath, Stanier, and Kinnersley families, and Earl Granville of Trentham Hall who took the initiative. H.H. Williamson of Greenway Bank Hall was considering building his own railway line when North Staffordshire Railway Company pre-empted his proposal by adding the Biddulph Valley Branch to their existing network between 1858 and 1860. With the line under construction, Williamson sank two new shafts at his Whitfield Colliery site. The mines were sold to a consortium shortly before Williamson's death. This group formed the Whitfield Colliery Company Limited in 1868 and were in turn bought out by Chatterley Iron Company in 1873, who added a private rail link to carry coal directly to their blast furnaces. An explosion in 1881, in which 24 men lost their lives, caused considerable damage. Two of the main shafts were closed. As production fell, financial problems escalated. Chatterley Iron was forced into administration. In 1883 the latest longwall mining techniques were introduced, and with production boosted to viable levels the Chatterley Whitfield Colliery Company was formed to take over the assets in 1891.

The 1st Earl Granville's Leveson-Gower ancestors had been involved in mining in the Hanley and Shelton district since taking on the balance of a lease of land owned by the Duchy of Lancaster in 1732. A developmental surge was triggered in 1839 when work began

81 *Coal tipping and screening equipment, 1878. Coal was delivered to an upper 'shaking box', small coal was sifted out through a screen and the remaining large pieces were loaded onto delivery trucks via a chute.*

on a bank of three blast furnaces between Cobridge Road and Mill Street (later renamed Etruria Road). Shelton Iron and Steel Company Limited was formed in 1866, with George, 2nd Earl Granville holding a controlling share. Robert Heath's Grange Colliery, Fox and Ward's Boothen Pit (later acquired by Shelton Iron and Steel), and the company's own Racecourse Pits at Etruria, Rowhurst Pits at Hanley, and the aptly named Deep Pit (over 1,500 feet) at Fair Green, were among surrounding suppliers of fuel for the furnaces. Also part of the Leveson-Gower industrial empire was the Stafford Iron and Coal Company, that had begun life as Great Fenton Iron and Coal Company, with Glebe Colliery and Stafford Colliery, Fenton, and Florence Colliery, Longton (named after the 3rd

82   *Pithead at Grove Colliery, with part of the screening and coal preparation plant in the foreground.*

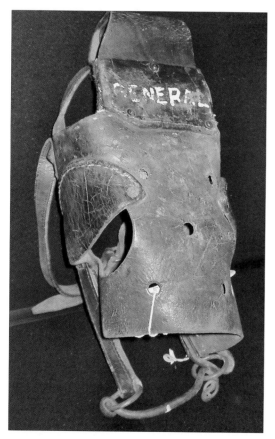

83   *Leather protective head guard with jointed snaffle bit, part of the harness worn by pit ponies.*

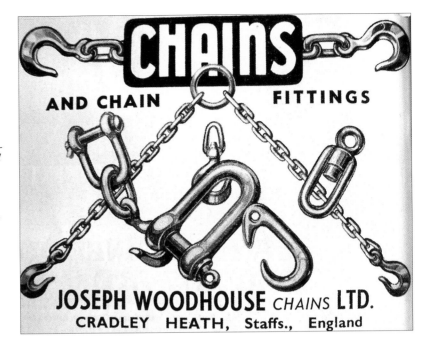

84 *Chainmaking was a traditional Black Country industry. Chains remained in use for haulage in smaller pits in South Staffordshire after most collieries had switched to steel wire ropes.*

Duke of Sutherland's daughter) part of the same business conglomeration.

By the end of the 19th century, when 'coal' had been added to the company name to form Shelton Iron Steel and Coal Company Limited, production in North Staffordshire was close to seven million tons a year. Shafts of 2,000 feet were common. North Staffordshire had the deepest pits in Western Europe. Sneyd Colliery, Florence Colliery and Stafford Colliery were all mining 2,600 feet or more below the surface.

Washing to remove dirt, and grading coal using jiggers, vibrating screens and picking belts was introduced in the late 19th century, just in time to meet with emerging environmental concern about pollution. A River Pollution Prevention Act passed in 1876 banned foul water being disposed of directly into waterways. W. Wardle described a pioneering shaker screen coal sorter designed by the manager at Essington Farm Colliery in the 1889 edition of his *Reference Book on Practical Mining*:

The principle of this screen is that of the threshing machine. An enormous tippler delivers the coal on the upper platform of a large 'swinging' or 'shaking' box, which is kept in motion laterally by a small steam engine. The platform consists of a lattice wire netting in lieu of ordinary screen bars, through which all the contents fall, except the largest, which is at once delivered down a shute into the trucks. There are three such platforms similarly constructed, and each delivering its own special size through a convenient 'spout' at which lads are placed to pick out inferior pieces; finally, the slack falls through the bottom into a truck.

Underground haulage by boys and ponies was made easier by the laying of rails. Tubs were fitted with flanged wheels to keep them on track. Boots were expensive and many men employed on haulage wore clogs. When rails were introduced, the clogs could be adapted using flattened cocoa tins nailed to the sole and angled to create a lip which allowed the men to ride the rails on tow behind tubs.

Ropes of woven hemp used for haulage had the safety benefit of showing visible signs of wear but chains were stronger. Perhaps because their manufacture was such a traditional Black Country industry (although small producers existed elsewhere and notably at Smallthorne in North Staffordshire), chains were in use in many small South Staffordshire pits until nationalisation. Elsewhere, and in all large collieries, steel wire ropes began replacing chains around 1880, greatly increasing the speed of winding. Before the introduction of cages from the 1840s, ponies were lowered in nets and men rode the haulage rope. Cages were in common use in the deep pits of North Staffordshire by the 1860s. Shaft guides provided stability. Steam-driven haulage, in limited use from the end of the 18th century, began to be widely adopted as the depth of mines increased. Two systems came into common use in main roadways. In 'main and tail', two drums were used, the 'main' winding full tubs 'outbye' and the 'tail' lowering empties 'inbye'. In the alternative 'endless' rope arrangement, a rope wound and unwound from a single drum and was returned by a wheel at the end of the roadway. Tubs were attached at intervals.

Winding engines were most commonly of the horizontal type but a small number of vertical engines requiring tall engine houses were also at work in Staffordshire. Two vertical winding engines from Manchester manufacturers Wren and Hopkinson operated at Stafford Colliery, one at Homer Upcast and the other at Sutherland Downcast, from 1875 until the pit closed in 1969. Engine houses were typically three storeys, built of brick and with a gable roof. A middle floor built around the cylinder head, and an upper loft affording access to the beam or 'bob', facilitated inspection and maintenance. Electric winders were developed by 1906 but not widely introduced in Staffordshire until after nationalisation.

Restrictions on boys working underground introduced by the Mines Act of 1842 increased the numbers of ponies employed. The same Act specified that stallions or geldings and not mares should be used. Ponies at small mines might be brought up at the end of every shift. Most were kept underground. Stables were always situated close to the air intake shaft. In circumstances where the face was a long distance from the shaft, additional stalls might be set up as a halfway house. Gin horses were large, powerful animals, often former railway or canal horses: 'Big as a pit bonk hoss' was a familiar Black Country description applied to anything of great size. Underground, pit ponies varied in size from 10 to 14 hands depending on the height of tunnels; the most horse that could be fitted into the available space was the aim. Welsh cobs, New Forest and Dartmoor ponies were a popular choice. Each animal had a unique name recorded in a horse book kept at the stable office and worked with the same driver. Ponies were invariably cold shod with ready-made shoes, the blacksmith working underground while the animals were groomed an hour or so before a shift was due to start. Most collieries employed their own blacksmith, part of a small maintenance team, who was also responsible for maintaining a sharp cutting edge on tools.

The relationship between pony and driver was close. Many drivers showed affection for their four-legged 'partners'. Others treated them with brutality. Visitors to the Cannock Chase Colliery's No. 3 Pit in 1908 gave a cosy view in an article carried by *The Gentleman's Review and Gentlewoman's Journal*:

85 *Cannock Chase pit ponies with their handlers. Only stallions or geldings worked underground.*

86 *Visitors preparing to descend one of Cannock Chase Colliery Company's pits, possibly the party who visited No. 3 Pit in 1908 and wrote an enthusiastic report of their experiences in* The Gentleman's Review and Gentlewoman's Journal.

87   *Champion pit pony Bob from Cannock Wood Colliery with miner Jim Childs. Pit ponies often went to local shows. Bob impressed at two Royal Shows and won a Horse of the Year rosette.*

So much is said about the lot of these little animals that we were careful to note their condition and treatment. They all seem well fed, and strange to say, well groomed, and nothing gave us greater pleasure than now and again to come across a boy driver who was giving his pony, as a tit-bit, some grass he had brought from above. Not one of the drivers had a stick or seemed to want one, and we heard their voices away in the distance long before they saw us and noted in the very tone the comradeship between these two workers underground.

A raft of provisions in the Coal Mines Act of 1911 included what was widely referred to as the 'Pit Ponies Charter'. The Act gave animals greater protection, stipulating limits to the hours they could work, specifying regular veterinary inspections

and a minimum age of four years, together with standards for feed and cleanliness of stables. Ponies were brought to the surface to enjoy fresh air and fields during annual holiday closures such as Wakes Weeks and 'Potters' Fortnight'. By the late 1930s, only 43 ponies remained at work underground in North Staffordshire; in South Staffordshire there were 447 and a further 929 at work in the Cannock Chase coalfield. Most ponies were found homes once they became surplus to requirements. Six long-serving ponies at Fair Lady Pit, some with more than 20 years' service, were put down despite miners' protests and left underground when the mine closed in 1965. The last few remaining pit ponies in Staffordshire were 'pensioned off' in the 1970s. Above ground, all large collieries had private rail networks and their own locomotives with steam giving way to diesel after nationalisation.

Naked flame safety lamps remained the industry standard throughout the 19th century. In the 1890s, carbide lamps largely supplanted those fuelled by tallow, paraffin wax or oil. A controlled drip of water reacting with a carbon compound produced acetylene, an illuminant gas. Lit by a spark from a built-in flint wheel striker, carbide lamps gave a clear, bright light. Electric safety lamps using a wet cell battery were first introduced in Staffordshire around 1912. Although they gave improved luminosity they were weighty and it was not until safety helmets became standard headgear in the late 1930s and lightweight cap lamps were developed, powered from a battery pack worn on the belt, that electric lamps replaced flame models. Davy-style lamps remained in common use for gas detection. Lowering the flame where methane is present produces a pale blue 'cap'. From the height and shape of the cap an experienced observer can estimate, with a fair degree of accuracy, the percentage of gas in the atmosphere. From 1939 various automatic firedamp detectors were approved for use. In some systems ignition of firedamp broke an electrical circuit, reducing power to dim a bulb and alerting the tester to the presence of flammable gas. Others worked by increased heat from a flame whenever methane was present completing a circuit contact that lit a red danger bulb. Electronic detectors, commonly called 'methanometers', were widely used from the 1970s.

Hand holing was the first operation to be mechanised. Various coal-cutting machines were available by the mid-1870s. One of the earliest automatic cutters was a Staffordshire design called the 'Simplex'. The inventor, English, an employee of Pelsall Iron Company, was encouraged to develop the machine by Edward Peake when the company was taken over by Walsall Wood Colliery in the 1890s.

88 *Early carbide lamp. A valve-controlled trickle of water from a container at the top of the pack reacted with carbide to give off acetylene, an illuminant gas. Lamps lasted for a full shift and produced a bright light.*

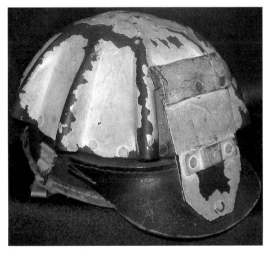

89 *Safety helmets became regulation headgear in the late 1930s.*

90 (left) *Davy-style safety lamps were used to detect firedamp. This training aid from Valley Colliery shows the height and shape of the blue cap produced by different percentages of methane in the atmosphere.*

91 (right) *Official's safety lamp (on the left). If the flame went out while testing for gas the tester was required to return to fresh air in the roadway before relighting the lamp. Above right: 'Ringrose' firedamp alarm battery lamp from Hem Heath Colliery. Automatic alarms incorporating an electrical circuit that was broken by ignition of firedamp were first approved in 1935.*

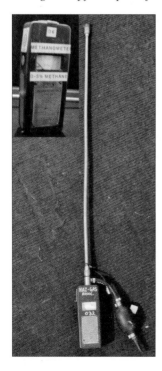

92 *Methane gas detector or 'methanometer' (Type HCIII) with extending probe, and (inset) hand-held detector (Type D6).*

After a successful trial, Florence Coal and Iron Company was one of the first collieries in North Staffordshire to switch to using mechanical cutters at the face, in the early-20th century. Cannock Chase Colliery Company were experimenting with a single machine in 1913 and had 30 in operation just five years later. By 1945 almost all coal in North Staffordshire and the bulk of production on Cannock Chase was mechanically cut using rotary cutters of either disc, bar or the more recently developed chain type, and mechanically conveyed and loaded using either compressed air or electrical power. Electrical power was more economical as well as easier to install and maintain, but particularly in the early days carried with it the risk of sparking. Where firedamp was present, more expensive compressed air power was a safer option. Sneyd Colliery

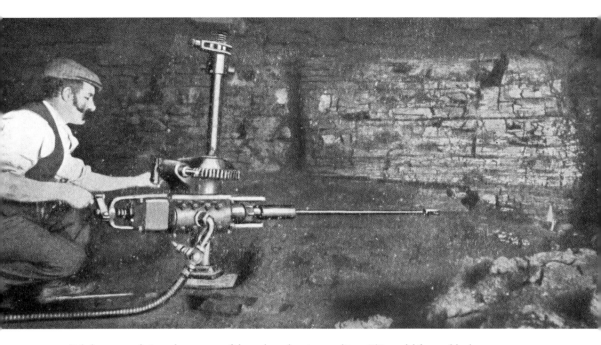

93   *Siskol compressed air coalcutter, one of the early coalcutting machines. This model featured both a rotary and percussive action and was popularly known as the 'pom pom' from the sound it made in use.*

pioneered research into wet cutting, using water pipes fixed to machinery to suppress volatile face dust. Automatic stone-dusters blew powdered shale or limestone to reduce the risk of suspended coal dust igniting in roadways.

In South Staffordshire mechanisation remained the exception. It was not that the Black Country was technologically backward: mechanical cutting worked best on narrow seams and was unsuitable for the unique Thick Coal of the South Staffordshire field.

As the 20th century progressed, iron production dipped and coal became the dominant partner in the 'twin enterprise'. The only survivor of the demise of Darlaston Steel and Iron Company in the 1890s had been Holly Bank Colliery. When serious fault disturbance threatened to prevent access to lower seam reserves, a winding shaft was sunk in Hilton Park and an underground link constructed that

came into production in 1924. It was the first all-electric pit in the Midlands. Miners were supplied with Oldham-type electric lamps. Five hundred houses were built to accommodate additional employees and their families. Adverse economic conditions threatened liquidation in 1930, but sufficient progress had been made to secure concessions under the Coal Mines Act of 1930, legislation which had aimed at encouraging small pits to amalgamate and agree joint district marketing schemes. A new company, Hilton Main Colliery, took over and production expanded. A new 1,900ft shaft begun in 1933 was nearing completion three years later when pit manager R.A. Voss paid tribute to the men of Francois Cementation, Doncaster who were carrying out the sinking operation:

They are a wonderful lot of men. These pit sinkers always excite my greatest admiration. They travel about the

94 *Motorised rock drills were in use at larger Staffordshire collieries from around 1900.*

95 *Automatic stone-dust spraying trolley used to suppress volatile coal dust in roadways.*

96 *Colliers at Hamstead, c.1900. Smoking was banned underground but miners frequently carried their pipes, often working with the stem clamped between their teeth.*

97   *Oldham 'bottle' lamps of the type in common use in the 1920s and 30s.*

country from one sinking to another, and everywhere they go they win friends and admirers of typical English grit and ability. They expect fair play, they like to be able to trust a boss's word, and they will put every ounce of strength into their work.

The deep mines of North Staffordshire continued to expand. New shafts were sunk at Holditch, always known locally as 'Brymbo' (1920), Wolstanton (1921), Parkhouse (1923), Hem Heath (1929) and Berry Hill (1932).

In 1933 the Coal Utilisation Council was established to promote British coal.

The following year import duties were imposed on oil to help bolster the industry. In 1937 Chatterley Whitfield became the first British mine to reach the singular production milestone of one million tons of coal in a single year. Between the end of the 1926 strike and 1939, North Staffordshire could boast the greatest increase in output per manshift in the country. Ninety-five per cent of coal was mechanically cut and almost all of it face conveyed. Production exceeded that of Cannock Chase and the rapidly contracting South Staffordshire field combined.

4
Say Not the Struggle Naught Availeth

Staffordshire's strong coalmining tradition was part of a diverse industrial base. With the arguable exception of Cannock Chase during the boom period from 1860 to 1890, when the population in some small towns grew tenfold, colliers were always part of a wider community, not isolated in separate mining villages. Competition between miners in the three coalfields developed out of pride in performance. Beyond this was a common bond, a fellow loyalty born out of shared experience. In the late 18th century, when workers in various trades were attempting to organise collectively to improve pay and conditions, solidarity put miners in pole position, but theirs was a difficult struggle. Successive governments were frightened of the potential subversive power of organised workers. In 1799 and 1800 Combination Acts prohibited two or more people joining together for the purpose of gaining higher wages or better conditions of work. To avoid contravening the law, miners formed 'friendly societies'.

Colliers in North Staffordshire, where there were fewer and bigger pits, found it easier to organise themselves than those in the more fragmented coal industry of the Black Country. In all areas success was limited. Coal owners refused to negotiate with organised groups and miners gained a reputation for resorting to threats and sabotage. Disputes involving the withdrawal of labour invariably petered

out acrimoniously when hardship and loss of earnings forced men back to work.

Pay tended to track the market, wages rising and falling with the price of coal. With small-scale shallow workings, it was relatively easy to respond to demand, suspending operations temporarily when there was a lull and re-opening when markets revived. Voluntary agreements to limit output were formalised between coalmasters in the same district.

In 1787 militant colliers in Bilston campaigned for an increase in pay to bring their wages to three shillings a day. Ten years later, with the Napoleonic Wars stimulating demand and coal vital for the war effort, wages reached four shillings a day. Victory at Waterloo in 1815 ended more than two decades of war with France but Britain was heavily in debt and the

98 *Hand-held drilling machine known as a 'pig's head' from the supposed resemblance of its handles and chuck to the ears and snout of a pig.*

economy slid into deep recession. Food shortages pushed up prices and the cost of living rose sharply. Discharged soldiers and sailors swelled the ranks of unemployed. Demand for manufactured goods melted away, jobs were lost and wage rates fell. Morris dancing was one among many inventive ways in which out-of-work miners sought to raise funds, adapting traditional airs to help make their point. A typical lyric of the day ran:

> O, the shilling
> O, the shilling
> We'd sooner starve
> Than go to work
> At a shilling a day.

In 1816, a group of unemployed Staffordshire colliers set off to draw attention to their situation by hauling three waggons of coal across country to London. *The Times* misread the public mood, commenting haughtily:

> It is utterly impossible that such wild projects should be attended with any beneficial result, which might not be much better obtained by remaining at home, and stating their grievances in writing to those who have it in their power to afford them relief.

The discipline and good humour displayed by the marchers won considerable support for the plight of the working classes caught up in the depression, and generous donations were collected. Protestors were not always as well behaved. Civil authorities had frequent recourse to the army and militia. On a number of occasions the Riot Act was read.

Repeal of the Combination Acts in 1824 and 1825 allowed miners to form district associations. With a buoyant market for coal, North Staffordshire's miners took

99 *Miner turning a manual ratchet drill through a metal pit prop prior to shotfiring.*

advantage of a good bargaining position to win concessions in 1825. But locally formed unions were generally short-lived. Groups of miners rallied around specific issues, but once the focus of conflict was resolved support and interest quickly faded. Colliery owners continued to refuse to recognise workers' associations.

Wage instability resulting from economic fluctuations was a constant source of unrest. Calling for unity in 1831, Staffordshire's miners appropriated Nelson's rallying cry at the Battle of Trafalgar, 'England expects that every man will do his duty.' A newly formed North Staffordshire Coalminers Union Society pressed for a wage increase and other benefits in May of that year. Coalmasters meeting at the *Legs of Man Inn* to discuss the situation presented a united front to a list of demands, issuing a notice declaring a rise out of the question. There was a sting in the tail:

> We therefore are unanimously determined to resist all and every such demands as have been this day submitted to this meeting by our workmen by every means in our power, and earnestly request our respective workmen, not to listen to the interested and pernicious counsel of others, and we also agree not to employ any person who shall be discharged by his employer as a consequence of being in the Trades Union, or shall have given notice for an increase in wages.

100 *Filling out fork. The gap between the tines allowed small coal to fall through when loading. Before power stations became major customers there was little demand for small coal and 'slack' was generally shovelled back into the waste.*

Well organised themselves, mine owners recognised the bargaining power of concerted effort and did all they could to disrupt fledgling unions. Threat of dismissal with no prospect of re-employment elsewhere was a powerful weapon. Under such intimidation, cohesion crumbled. A handbill putting the case for the Miners' Union Society lamented the actions of those who gave in to employer pressure, drawing a biblical comparison of betrayal:

> … observe, in the midst of our conflicts as the chief priests and scribes sought means to destroy Jesus, so our masters and agents are seeking traitors, and to our great astonishment and to their disgrace they have found Judas's and behold the very men that betrayed us, sat with us at the table on the 25th of May 1831, but behold on the 26th of May, those traitors were absent.

Against a background of falling coal prices, a meeting at Wednesbury in November 1831 attracted an audience of nearly three thousand. Rowdy confrontations took place at a number of Black Country pits.

Recession hit industrialists as well as employees. A conference held in December by coal owners in West Bromwich to discuss a rapidly worsening economic situation was reported in the *Wolverhampton Chronicle*:

> We have no doubt that many of the colliers [and others] are suffering great privations. It is notorious that the present low prices are ruinous to the masters, and undoubtedly the men must also suffer, but we must also state that many of those who have least ground for complaint have been the foremost in disorderly proceedings.

As 1831 drew to a close, a series of stoppages aimed at securing higher wages took place. Secondary action was stepped up. Flying pickets toured Staffordshire organising lines of striking miners to try and discourage those willing to work from entering collieries. The scale of disturbances escalated. Pit ropes were cut, engines sabotaged and coal barges scuttled. Additional special constables were hurriedly recruited. When the leader of a militant group was arrested the authorities were powerless to prevent a mob breaking down the door of Bilston lock-up and setting him free. A demonstration in Wolverhampton Market Place descended into a mini-riot, with coal carts overturned and stones thrown. The army and militia were mobilised. Troops under the Earl of Plymouth arrested 17 miners during a confrontation at Dudley on 3 December 1831. Three days later, a group of colliers dug in on a pit bank at Oldbury responded with a shower of stones when they were charged by troops with bayonets fixed. After weeks of conflict and deprivation endured by striking miners and their families, a small rise of six pence per day was offered, the rise to be funded by increasing the retail price of coal. There were those who held out for a little longer, arguing for a more equitable deal. Others returned to work, and with unity crumbling hopes of a better result were lost.

Truck arrangements, more widespread in Staffordshire than elsewhere in the country, were a recurrent source of grievance. Parliament took action in 1817 to end the custom, but vested interests blocked the fundamental reform of employment law necessary for change and the system continued in practice. A Parliamentary Bill sponsored by Edward Littleton, MP for Stafford and a leading Staffordshire coalmaster (later Lord Hatherton), strengthening legislation against the practice of trucking, was enacted in 1832.

Mine owners and colliers experienced inconsistency from the courts. Landowning gentry, clergymen and bankers made up 90 per cent of serving county magistrates in Staffordshire in 1832, a mix that produced a degree of compassion for the working classes tempered with strict enforcement of the law on Sunday observance. Industrialists, it was felt, if appointed to the Bench might

101 *Brass 'button' disc indicating membership of Cannock Miners' Association, 1925.*

be tempted to put their own economic interests above the requirements of law. Littleton's Truck Bill tried to tackle this by including a clause that stated adjudication in cases brought under the legislation had to be heard by impartial justices. Coal owners felt magistrates, many of whom were openly sympathetic to the difficulties faced by working miners, did not always give them a fair hearing. In 1821 Reverend Alexander Haden, vicar of Wednesbury and an active member of the County Bench, had made his views clear in a letter addressed to Staffordshire MP and Home Secretary Sir Robert Peel, condemning an increase in truck prices implemented by the coalmasters of Wolverhampton. However, the following year, adjudicating between striking colliers from Ettingshall and Monmore Green, Haden refused to accept grievances caused by the truck system in mitigation and convicted nine miners charged with incitement to riot.

Market fluctuations continued to influence pay and colliers were quick to press for an increase when demand was high, as a report in the *Wolverhampton Chronicle* of 1846 makes clear:

> The demand for coal is now found to exceed the supply throughout the entire district, and a general advance in price has been the natural consequence. Best qualities have risen 10d. per ton within the last week, and the workmen have received an addition so their wages range from 4s. to 5s. per day. When this advance has not been freely awarded, the men are in a restless and agitated state, and partial strikes have taken place.

Colliery owners responded by imposing unanimously agreed reductions as soon as economic conditions took a downturn. In 1861 the *Staffordshire Advertiser* gave details of a meeting held at the Earl of Dudley's Round Oak Ironworks to discuss cutting miners' wages:

> The low price of minerals, the quantity of foreign goods in the market, and the general depression existing in the staple trades of the district were given for the reduction. About twenty representatives of the trade were present. Considerable discussion took place, but eventually it was unanimously decided that a reduction should be made in the wages of mine colliers of 3d. per day. This movement will, we understand, be participated in by employers in other portions of the South Staffordshire district.

Miners were among supporters of a working-class movement for political reform known as Chartists (after the so-called 'People's Charter' outlining their demands) who attacked colliery property and broke into Hanley police station. The Chartist riots exposed the inadequacies of a hard-pressed judicial system and opened the door for changes on the County Bench.

102   *Men posing in a 'bowk' or bucket at one of the Earl of Dudley's Himley Colliery shafts in the early 20th century.*

The Marquis of Anglesey, himself a leading Staffordshire colliery owner, marked his five-year term as Lord Lieutenant of the county by deliberately commissioning industrialists as justices. By the time fellow aristocratic coal owner Lord Hatherton took over from the Marquis, in 1854, over half of all magistrates were iron or coalmasters.

Increasingly, disputes were extending beyond individual pits. Colliers outside areas directly involved were beginning to take action in support of fellow miners. A dispute over wages in 1842 led to a widespread withdrawal of labour across the county and, in North Staffordshire, to aggressive demonstrations. When miners at Bell's Mill Pit in the Potteries stopped work in 1851, in an attempt to increase their wages by six pence a day

103 *Shaft top, Mid Cannock Colliery, c.1920. Two miners are about to descend with their lamps and snap tins clipped to the chain.*

and raise their pay to the local average, other local miners came out in sympathy. Cannock Chase recorded its first strike in 1858. North Staffordshire miners fought bitter five-month-long battles against pay reductions in 1861, 1878 and again in 1883. Each time hardship eventually forced them back to work. There were stoppages in South Staffordshire in 1858, 1864, 1874 and 1884. An unemployed Bilston collier summed up the situation during the 1878 depression in song:

> The masters and the public say
> The trade has left the land,
> Both coal and wages must come down,
> If not the work must stand.
>
> They tell us very plainly, too,
> They mean to use their powers
> In bringing us poor miners back
> To slavery and long hours.

> But should reductions come again,
> I feel in duty bound
> To ask that those should be reduced
> Who get their thousand pound.

Rumour and counter rumour constantly circulated, adding to industrial unrest. An unconfirmed report in the newspapers of North Staffordshire that Robert Heath, local MP and mine owner, had offered his employees a 10 per cent pay rise created uproar in July 1878. Heath speedily quashed the rumour as ludicrous, complaining, 'If only the state of trade allowed such consideration.' In the same year the Association of Colliery Owners of Cannock Chase jointly agreed to cut production until the market recovered, stating, 'No one can justify the unbridled squandering of valuable mineral property.'

In the mid-19th century few children from working-class families went to school. Half the population could not read or write. The Victorian concept of moral improvement and the need for an educated working class in an increasingly technical industrialised world provided impetus for change. The first national movement in adult education began in the 1820s with the founding of Mechanics' Institutes. Funded by subscription, they organised lectures and classes. Many contained libraries and reading rooms where local and national newspapers, as well as periodicals, were available. The Cannock Chase Colliery Company built its own school that operated with the aid of a government grant. Across the county, miners' schools were established with scholarships for high achieving pupils.

An Education Act of 1870 made school compulsory for children from the ages of 5 to 13 years. It did not make education free. Not until 1891 did free schooling begin, and then only at first for infants. Local School Boards were established and a number of new schools were built, many in Staffordshire's mining districts. One of these was Chadsmoor Board School, which opened for boys in 1886 and a year later for girls. A letter to the *Cannock Advertiser* in 1887 signed simply 'A Collier's Wife' summed up one view of the difficulties that hard-pressed families now faced:

> Sir, I am a collier's wife, and live at Chadsmoor. I am mother to eight children, none of them old enough to work; some of them are big enough, but the School Board forces them to go to school till they are almost big enough to get married, and now sir, I want to ask how is this. How can I be expected to pay my way on the miserable wages earned by my husband? He works at the West Cannock Colliery, where everybody knows the men are only half paid for what they do. Now I have been forced to keep two of my lads away from the school for a week or two, for they have not any clothes to go in, let alone

> pay the fees. I have been brought up too respectable to attend the Board like a pauper, and ask for an excusing order, and the attendance man says if I don't send them to school he shall summon me.

The colourful view of the Victorian Staffordshire coalminer as hard-bitten, hard-drinking spendthrift with no thought for tomorrow was widely held and partly deserved. Of miners in general, the *Mining Journal* observed in 1857:

> It is the first duty of every man to make provision for his family, and upon no one of the labouring classes is this duty more incumbent than upon miners, for their lives, to use a technical phrase, are doubly hazardous; yet, according to the official returns, they would appear to be far behind the rest of the population in providing for themselves and families against accident.

Many miners took advantage of evening classes to improve their lot. George Goring (*c.*1849-1927), a miner from Heath Hayes, is a good example of what was possible for a hard-working, thrifty, ambitious miner of humble origins. He taught himself to read and write before going on to study a wide range of subjects including economics, history, geography and religion at night school. His wife sold surplus home-grown fruit and vegetables from their front room. The Gorings saved enough to purchase not only their own house but also two neighbouring properties. Miners led the way in working-class home ownership.

In a job that depended on teamwork it is hardly surprising to find this translated into activities outside work. Collieries had a tradition of choirs, brass bands and other social, sporting and recreational activities.

Structured trade unionism in the coal industry began in 1842 with the formation

104 *Aerial view of Cannock Wood Colliery, 1930. Cannock Wood was judged to be uneconomic and closed in 1973.*

of the Miners' Association of Great Britain and Ireland. An emerging railway network was making it easier to move coal around the country, adding to the pressure for effective local organisation and national representation. Lanarkshire miner-turned-teacher Alexander MacDonald founded the National Association of Coal, Lime and Ironstone Miners of Great Britain in 1851. This organisation became the Miners' National Union in 1863, with MacDonald as president. An alternative Amalgamated Association of Miners, established in 1869, gained little support and soon vanished from the scene.

Miners needed representation at the highest level. MacDonald stood as Liberal Party candidate for Stafford in the General Election of 1874. His election, and that of fellow miner Thomas Burt as MP for Morpeth, saw the first working-class members take their seats in the House of Commons. District unionisation in Staffordshire took its first steps with the South Staffordshire and East Worcestershire Amalgamated Miners' Association in 1863. North Staffordshire Miners' Federation (1869), Old Hall and Highley District Miners' Association (1883), Pelsall District Miners' Association (1887) and Cannock Chase Miners', Engineers' and Surfacemen's Association (1887) followed. By the close of the 1880s a Midland Counties Federation was forging links between Staffordshire's district groups and others. In 1889, with the price of coal rising, a national meeting at Newport discussed wage bargaining tactics. A new union, the Miners' Federation of Great Britain (MFGB), was the outcome. The aim of the MFGB was to act as an umbrella body, uniting all mining trade unions. Although

105 *Conduit Colliery Company's No. 3 Pit in 1914. The Guibal fan house is in the centre of the picture.*

it marked the beginning of a much more powerful bargaining position it was not until after the Coal Mines Act of 1908, and the absorption of all independent local associations by the MFGB, that this aspiration became a reality.

Support for trade unionism was slow to take off. Little more than half of Staffordshire's miners were union members by the start of the 20th century. Official figures from the Labour Department of the Board of Trade showed union membership in the Black Country at only 20 per cent in 1901, probably an under-estimate but still low compared to 69 per cent in the country overall.

Colliery owners were swift to react to the setting up of the MFGB, forming a new joint body, the National Association of Great Britain, to co-ordinate responses to wage claims. The MFGB was prominent in a series of strikes in 1891 aimed at fighting wage reductions. Settlements were rapidly reached in North and South Staffordshire. Elsewhere negotiations continued. Cannock Chase coalfield had largely avoided the disruption that punctuated labour relations elsewhere in the county but national unity was increasingly involving miners in disputes that went beyond local issues. When protracted talks failed to secure a satisfactory deal, colliery owners on Cannock Chase found themselves facing an all-out stoppage for the first time as miners joined the 'Great Federation Lock Out' of 1893. That particular dispute lasted for 16 weeks until the government stepped in with the offer of a return to pre-strike wage rates pending a report by an independent Conciliation Board and a promise to act on the contentious issue of check weighmen and ensure there was provision for men

106 *Mounted police keep an eye on striking miners involved in a local dispute at Chesterton, North Staffordshire in 1910.*

and managers to approve appointments jointly. Check weighmen verified output at the pithead on which wages and bonuses were based. It was an invidious position. Accusations of compromised integrity and deliberately under-recorded tonnages were common. The Conciliation Board continued to operate relatively successfully for almost two decades.

In 1912 Staffordshire colliers again downed tools in support of the MFGB's principal objective of a national minimum wage. Violence broke out in the Potteries. A group of miners overran Silverdale Colliery, smashing windows in the offices, maintenance shops and stores. An offer to appoint District Boards with responsibility for setting regional rates was put to the ballot with a recommendation by the MFGB leadership to accept the proposal. Staffordshire, by now part of a

Midland Federation including Shropshire, Warwickshire and Worcestershire, with a total union membership of 36,900, voted by a substantial majority in favour of a return to work. Nationally, the vote was to continue the strike. An embarrassed MFGB executive committee decided that as there was no provision in the rules for the size of majority needed for a vote to be carried they would set one retrospectively at two-thirds. With the 'No' vote falling short of this target, they were able to declare the strike settled and order an immediate return to work. Public sympathy for miners, always fickle, had in any case drained away. A rather condescending editorial in the *Colliery Guardian* of 8 March 1912 was scathing:

People are only seeing now what some of us have seen for years – that the miner, excellent fellow though he is, is

107 *Miners digging for coal on an outcropping seam in North Staffordshire during the strike of 1912.*

extremely selfish as a class ... he wants no help from outside; but he will also give none, except to his fellows, and not always then.

The same piece contained a nugget of truth about the attitudes and culture most miners would recognise:

> ... he [the miner] is capable of supreme acts of heroism in the pit; his affection for his kith and kin and his dogs is great; whilst perfectly contented with his own lot, he will lay down his tools to support an underpaid fellow miner, without regard to the latter's capacity or industry, or to gain the day for his brethren in another county.

An unquestioning sense of loyalty and shared values whose importance transcended mere logic was beyond the comprehension of many outside the industry.

The outbreak of the First World War in 1914 began a coalmining boom. Fuel was vital to the war effort and the government took over financial control of the industry. Wages were high and coal production reached a peak. Many small mines that had been closed as unprofitable became viable again and were re-opened. Peace in 1918 marked a harsh return to economic reality. Over-production and competition between coalfields caused prices to plummet. High inflation and a worldwide trade slump made matters worse. Faced with falling output, low prices, an urgent need for investment to make British coal competitive on the export market, and the prospect of control being handed back to the coal owners, the MFGB Annual

108   *Coal picking at Apedale during the 1912 strike.*

Conference in July 1919 decided to pursue a 30 per cent pay increase, a two-hour reduction in the working day (the Coal Mines Regulation Act of 1908 had set a general limit for working underground of eight hours including winding time), and nationalisation of the industry. Robert Smillie, President of the MFGB, declared, 'What we want to do is reconstruction in the interests of the country.'

Strike action was averted when the Prime Minister, David Lloyd George, appointed a Royal Commission under the chairmanship of Sir John Sankey to investigate miners' pay and conditions. The Sankey Commission was given a wide brief to consider all options

> for the future organisation of the coal industry, whether on the present basis, or on the basis of joint control, nationalisation, or any other basis.

Miners accepted an interim recommendation proposing a 20 per cent wage rise and a seven-hour working day while the Sankey Commission continued to consider the question of future organisation. By the time they concluded in favour of nationalisation, the introduction of new pay and conditions had calmed the mood. There was no resistance when the government decided not to act on the Commission's suggestion and to leave the mines in private ownership.

A strike in pursuit of a wage claim in 1920 resulted in a temporary pay rise pending agreement on a substantive deal. The MFGB was keen to secure a national settlement. Acting for the owners, the National Association of Great Britain wanted separate pay rates in each coalfield, to reflect variances in productivity and coal quality. Talks ended in stalemate and a strike was called for 1 April 1921. With the rest of the country experiencing high unemployment, there was little public sympathy for the miners. A cartoon in *Punch* illustrated the general mood. It

109   *Surviving Victorian workshops and two-storey office block of New Hawne Colliery begun by the New British Iron Company in 1864. 'New' distinguished the operation from an existing Hawne Colliery that was known afterwards as 'Old' Hawne. New Hawne flooded when pumping was suspended during a strike in 1921 and was subsequently abandoned.*

showed a miner addressing a locked out factory worker: 'Well mate, we're both in the same fix,' to which the factory hand replies, 'Ho – are we? Your door's open and you've got the key of the mine.' Promised support from railway and transport workers (the so-called 'Triple Alliance') failed to materialise.

A State of Emergency was declared as the stoppage began to take its toll. Workers were put on short time or laid off as fuel shortages closed industry down. Troops were put on standby and guards posted at coal depots. Appeals to allow pumping and tanking operations to continue were rejected. On 9 April the *Dudley Chronicle* reported:

> Incalculable damage has already been done and if some move which will restart the colliery pumps within the next 24 hours is not taken South Staffordshire will cease to be a great coal-producing area.

This was not scaremongering but stark reality. New Hawne and Timbertree were two of the larger collieries among a number of concerns in the Black Country irreparably damaged by floodwater that would never reopen.

As the strike continued into the summer of 1921, miners' families faced destitution. Coal mounds were 'picked'. Strikers began unofficial mining operations, digging outcrops and sinking small pits. Hardship made defeat inevitable. Miners returned to work on 4 July. Staged short-term reductions in pay were imposed and 22 District Boards established to set area-based pay rates. It was a bitter lesson and worse was to come. World trade doldrums continued to adversely affect the British economy. In 1925 mine owners announced plans for further wage reductions. This time the Trade Union Congress (TUC) promised its backing for miners. Threatened with widespread industrial action, the Conservative administration of Stanley Baldwin intervened, undertaking to subsidise miners' pay at current rates for a period of nine months while yet another Royal Commission, this time under the chairmanship of Sir Herbert Samuel, looked into ongoing problems in the coal industry.

The Samuel Commission published its findings in March 1926, recommending the subsidy should be withdrawn and wages reduced. Colliery owners drew up new terms of employment offering increased hours coupled with a reduction in wages. It was a non-negotiable, take it or leave it, offer. A deadline was set for Saturday 1 May. A TUC meeting held on that day voted for a general strike in support of the miners subject to the TUC taking over negotiations. On 3 May around 20 per cent of the national workforce came out on strike. Stoppages hit the railways, docks, foundries, building sites and newspapers. To keep the country running, the government introduced emergency regulations. Mail was diverted from rail to road and electricity supplies were reduced. The country was divided into 10 administrative areas, Staffordshire being covered from Birmingham.

Appeals were made not to hoard coal but supplies were soon in short supply and rationing was imposed. A request was issued for volunteers to maintain essential services. Placards emphasised that this was not strike breaking, but in the interests of the community. Four days into the strike Sir Herbert Samuel met a TUC negotiating committee and hammered out a deal. Under the agreement the wage subsidy would be reinstated pending the introduction of a national minimum wage guarantee set by an independent National Wages Board. It was acknowledged this would probably involve a reduction. Proposals to assist miners find alternative

110 'The subsidised mine owner – poor beggar!' (1925) redrawn from a cartoon published in the trade union Unity magazine, one of a number of lampoons that appeared in the wake of proposals to cut miners' wages.

jobs as the industry contracted were also included.

On 11 May TUC leaders accepted the package and called off the General Strike from the following day. Within a week all emergency committees had been disbanded and most of the country returned to normal working. Infuriated at not being consulted, the Miners' Federation accused the TUC of tamely surrendering and 'selling out' their members. Their slogan was 'Not a penny off the pay, not a second on the day,' and they rejected the offer. But now the miners stood alone. In June the Seven Hours Act was suspended, opening the way for a return to a longer working day. Local strike committees were formed. MFGB General Secretary Arthur Cook visited Staffordshire to rally support, with fiery calls for unity at mass meetings held in each of the coalfields. Sir Francis

III   *Families picking coal on the spoil heap at West Cannock No. 3 Pit during the prolonged strike of 1926.*

Joseph, Chairman of North Staffordshire Chamber of Commerce, called Cook a 'humble disciple of Lenin and Trotsky, playing to public fear of ulterior motives and Bolshevik tendencies'.

While dwindling reserves lasted, strikers received 10s. a week from union funds. Wives and children qualified for poor relief payments. Single men were also considered for poor relief in extreme circumstances but only if a written undertaking were given that any allowance would be repaid. Across the county, Boards of Guardians in charge of poor relief ran into financial problems. Many had to apply for overdrafts, increase the locally raised Poor Rate, and cut allowances in order to balance their books. A number of distress funds were set up.

Tensions rose. A fatal shooting followed a confrontation during illegal outcropping at Wetley Common, Bucknall. North Staffordshire miners' representative F.J. Hancock was formally asked to intervene

in order to stop miners digging on land belonging to Mossfield Colliery. Some outcrops proved highly productive, allowing a few lucky groups to make more money from their improvised do-it-yourself shafts than they could ever hope to earn as employed miners. But most struggled to provide for themselves and their families. A gin at Ellowes Colliery, Lower Gornal claimed to be the last still working in Staffordshire when the pit closed in 1926, but others left idle were pressed into illicit service by miners working seams on their own account. Working men's clubs gave food vouchers and provided meals. Soup kitchens struggled to meet demand. Churches offered prayers for a speedy resolution to the dispute. Church leaders held a national meeting with miners' representatives, after which the Bishop of Lichfield, Dr J.A. Kempthorne, wrote to the Prime Minister urging him to restore the subsidy and re-open negotiations.

Baldwin held firm, declaring the dispute was now for the two sides to settle.

Severe hardship began to force a slow return back to work. On 11 June James Cadman, Managing Director of Brereton Colliery, called a meeting at Rugeley's Drill Hall with Roy Wilson, MP for Lichfield Division, as guest speaker. Cadman, aware that with the strike biting demand for coal was high, offered pre-strike wages and a bonus to miners returning to work for as long as coal prices remained at a premium. North Staffordshire Colliery Owners Association made an offer on 9 July for a return to work with no reduction in pay but with an extra hour on the working shift.

There were angry confrontations between miners returning to work and those remaining on strike. Wives became involved. Those accepting the terms faced large numbers of pickets. One hundred and twenty men who turned up for work at Brereton had need of a police escort. The Riot Act was read at colliery gates. The Board of Guardians at Newcastle-under-Lyme became the first to stop poor relief payments, claiming the men had jobs to go to if they so chose. At the end of November most miners were back at work. By Christmas the strike was over. Those owing money to Poor Law Unions had their wages attached until 'loans' were repaid. Colliery proprietors charged a commission of five per cent for collecting the debt. Those who held out until the bitter end faced victimisation. Some never worked as miners again. In 1927 the Trade Disputes and Trade Union Act banned mass picketing and sympathetic industrial action.

When the MFGB became the National Union of Mineworkers (NUM), on 1 January 1945, the majority of miners in Staffordshire and elsewhere were members, a position that ensured a powerful

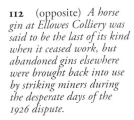

112 (opposite) *A horse gin at Ellowes Colliery was said to be the last of its kind when it ceased work, but abandoned gins elsewhere were brought back into use by striking miners during the desperate days of the 1926 dispute.*

113 (right) *Parkhouse Colliery, Chesterton in 1965. Three years later severe flooding led to closure.*

bargaining position and made the NUM a significant influence in the trade union movement.

It was not until 1972 that Staffordshire's miners were once more called out as part of a national strike. At a time of rampant inflation, and government policies aimed at pegging wage increases, the NUM Annual Conference held in autumn 1971 agreed to press for a 43 per cent pay rise, and in the meantime instigated an overtime ban. To counter inflation the government set a cap on all pay deals of eight per cent. After a 7.9 per cent offer was rejected, the NCB halted negotiations and the NUM set 9 January 1972 for strike action. To stop the movement of coal and increase the impact of the stoppage, power stations and fuel depots were picketed. An angry confrontation between police and miners, as pickets successfully turned back lorries delivering coke supplies to the West Midlands Gas Board's Saltley Marsh depot

in Birmingham, raised issues that would eventually be tackled by laws making secondary picketing illegal. A State of Emergency was declared on 9 February and a three-day working week introduced to conserve electricity. A revised pay offer was accepted following a ballot and miners returned to work on 28 February. The deal put miners back at the top of the industrial wages league and underlined the economic importance of coal.

Within a year, a round of inflationary pay increases in other industries had eroded the gains and left miners once more playing catch-up. With the government threatening a freeze on pay, and a new Industrial Relations Act before Parliament, talks on miners' pay failed to reach an agreement. A ban on overtime began in November 1973 and on 9 February 1974 miners were again called out on strike. A three-day week was re-imposed. Conservative Prime Minister

114 *Brass pay check, Wimblebury Colliery. Checks or tallies were exchanged for lamps at the start of a shift and given back when the lamp was returned. Two-check systems were introduced in the 19th century to ensure an accurate record of numbers underground. Check systems were later adapted as a means of recording shifts and confirming identity for pay purposes.*

Edward Heath announced a snap general election, intended to give him a mandate for tough action, but defeat brought a Labour administration to power. A pay deal was rapidly agreed and a return to work followed. It was an epic victory. The deal went beyond pay to include improved pension arrangements, compensation for miners contracting pneumoconiosis, and qualified guarantees on jobs. With every demand met, there were those in the NUM hierarchy rumoured to have argued for holding out a little longer to give them time to think up more.

By 1983 use of oil and natural gas had reduced dependence on coal. The prospect of job losses and colliery closures was looking increasingly likely. This time a Conservative government under Margaret Thatcher was prepared for industrial action. In 1978, while in opposition, shadow minister Nicholas Ridley had drawn up plans to switch transport to roads in the event of a stoppage in the coal industry. Since then, stockpiles had been built up at power stations and imports stepped up.

In 1982 Arthur Scargill was elected to succeed Joe Gormley as president of the NUM in a landslide victory. A special delegate conference was held to consider action in pursuit of a pay claim and the protection of miners' jobs. A pithead ballot followed, asking

> Are you in favour of the special conference recommendation that the National Executive Committee be given authority to take industrial action (if necessary) to prevent the closure of any pit, plant or unit (other than on grounds of exhaustion) and at the same time bring about a satisfactory settlement of our wages claim?

This question met with a 'No'. A few months later, NUM delegates did vote in favour of an overtime ban to take effect from November 1983. Few would have anticipated it marking the start of one of the most bitter and divisive industrial struggles. From the beginning, winders in North Staffordshire opposed the ban and continued to work normally; setting the scene for divisions between moderate and militant miners that became a feature of the dispute. Winders using a side entrance at Hem Heath to avoid pickets became involved in a scuffle that led to the first arrests. Arthur Scargill visited Silverdale to make a typically impassioned plea for unity and solidarity. There were disagreements within the NUM over what counted as overtime and what was essential maintenance, but the ban attracted support from the majority of Staffordshire's miners. Coal production was significantly down. Jim Colgan, newly elected General Secretary of the Midlands Area NUM, observed that banning overtime 'was a very successful way of putting hardship on the Coal Board rather than on the men'.

115   *Silverdale Colliery, 1970. Miners at Silverdale repeatedly set output records throughout the 1970s. Closure in 1998 marked the end of seven centuries of deep mining in Staffordshire.*

116   *Octagonal brass pay checks, Hawkins Colliery.*

Against the background of this ongoing dispute, on 5 March 1984 Ian MacGregor, Chairman of the NCB, announced plans to close 20 pits considered uneconomic with the consequent loss of 20,000 jobs. Miners at Cortonwood Colliery in Yorkshire, top of the closure list, walked out at midnight. Scargill issued a call for all miners to strike. In the next few days, flying pickets visited collieries at Lea Hall, Littleton, Florence, Hem Heath, Holditch, Silverdale and Wolstanton in an effort to rally support.

Within a week over half the miners in the country (around 187,000) had joined in the action. A majority of Staffordshire's miners joined the initial stoppage. Many returned when Scargill refused to hold a national ballot although the overtime ban continued to be observed.

Rule 43 of the NUM constitution required a ballot. The decision to act without one made the strike technically illegal and opened the way for legal challenges, allowing the courts to seize

117   *Wolstanton Colliery, 1970s. The deepest pit in western Europe, Wolstanton topped the national Safety League in 1979.*

NUM assets and providing justification for aggressive policing. By the end of March a number of arrests and loyalty to fellow miners combined to entrench positions. Both sides were ready for a prolonged battle. No one believed it would last for almost a full year. A Strike Centre at 46 Harvey Road, Handsacre was one of several set up across the county to co-ordinate action. The NUM threatened to withdraw union membership from working miners. The NCB countered with assurances that jobs would not be affected if this happened.

Colliery managers in Staffordshire initiated an active campaign to urge those still on strike to return to work. Miners received individual letters. Special buses were laid on to make negotiating picket lines less personally confrontational. A degree of success for these measures attracted the media spotlight. In response, the NUM stepped up picketing in the county and extended activities to the power stations of the Trent Valley. Weekly mass meetings were held to keep striking miners informed. As hardship

set in support groups were formed. Miners' wives ran emergency food centres, held jumble sales, organised sponsored walks and joined in picketing. Teams of miners went out logging for firewood on Cannock Chase. Workers in other industries, individuals and community groups made donations to strike funds. Arts groups held fund-raising concerts, musicians busked, and collections were held on streets and in pubs. Sympathetic rail workers refused to transport coal. Arthur Scargill continued to tour the coalfields, speaking twice at meetings in Hanley alongside local NUM officials.

There was no doubting Scargill's fervour, but the campaign he orchestrated was tactically flawed. A gradual drift back to work raised bitter tensions. In October the National Association of Colliery Overmen, Deputies and Shotfirers (NACODS), who had continued to work throughout, voted by a large majority to strike in a move that would have closed all pits. In the event they won concessions and called off their proposed action. By November the strike

118 *Pithead showers, Littleton Colliery.*

was crumbling. Violent scuffles took place. Mounted police charged picket lines. Buses carrying working miners were attacked. When Labour Party leader Neil Kinnock joined Arthur Scargill at a meeting in Stoke Town Hall at the end of November more than three-quarters of miners were back at work, although production remained at little more than 25 per cent of pre-dispute tonnage. Those remaining on strike refused to abandon the struggle and continued until a special NUM conference voted by a slender majority (98 to 91) for a return to work on 5 March 1985. On the morning of 11 March the last strikers marched in to their collieries shoulder to shoulder. The dispute was over without

a settlement. Three weeks later the offer on the table outstanding from 1983 was accepted and a pay deal for 1984 agreed. A group of miners' wives formed the North Staffordshire Miners' Wives Action Group, continuing to campaign for the future of the local industry and on wider issues of social justice.

In divided communities tensions remained high. Working miners had set up a breakaway Union of Democratic Mineworkers (UDM) during the dispute, in opposition to the strike. The power base of the new union was Nottinghamshire. Returning miners elsewhere had begun to join as the strike continued. There was little support for the UDM in Staffordshire.

119   *Canteen, Lea Hall Colliery.*

120   *Aluminium pay check, No. 3 Pit, Littleton Colliery.*

On 10 March Arthur Scargill addressed a meeting at Lea Hall Colliery. A meeting so soon after the end of the strike attracted huge media interest. Charismatic and combative as ever, despite defeat, Scargill gave a trademark speech of defiance to rousing applause.

A decade later the industry was a mere shadow of its former self. As membership declined the NUM lost its automatic place on the TUC General Council. The UDM was no longer a splinter group but a fully-fledged union in its own right. Just 17 working collieries remained nationally and the remnants of Staffordshire's coal industry had been parcelled up and privatised.

121   *Commemorative badge issued to mark the 20th anniversary of the 1984/5 strike.*

5
Nationalisation and the End of an Era

Staffordshire's young, fit miners answered the call to join the armed services when war with Germany began in September 1939. Women were brought in to work on washing and screening plant. With large numbers of men unemployed, the government believed any manpower shortage underground would be temporary, but they were wrong. Applying an Essential Work Order to coal in 1941 in an effort to retain employees and persuade ex-miners to return to the industry had little impact. When the government took direct control in 1942, energy shortages were acute and having a detrimental effect on strategically important industries. To counter the problem, Minister of Labour Ernest Bevin launched a scheme in 1943 that allowed conscripts to volunteer for work in the mines rather than military service, and compulsorily redirected 10 per cent of all male conscripts aged 18-25 to work at collieries. Selection was by ballot.

Kemball Training Colliery, Fenton became one of 13 national training centres where recruits, known as 'Bevin Boys', underwent four weeks intensive skills training supplemented by classes at North Staffordshire Technical College. Allocation to a pit for a further two weeks instruction followed before work began for real. Accommodation was provided in hostels and in some cases billets were arranged in private houses. Most recruits were employed on haulage. A few progressed to working at the coalface. It was 1948 before the last of the Bevin Boys was demobilised. At the time there was no official recognition and no medals struck to acknowledge the vital role they played, and not until the 50th anniversary of the Second World War were Bevin Boys belatedly honoured. Unlike regular servicemen, they did not have the right to return to their former employment. Even so, hardly any stayed in mining once released.

Displaced Polish citizens swelled the ranks of Staffordshire's miners in the late 1940s, refugees escaping Russian occupation joining those who had earlier fled Nazism. Former army huts at Blackshaw Moor, Leek were pressed into use as a resettlement camp. In 1947 the Polish Resettlement Act gave émigrés the right to work. Many chose mining. The NUM had initially opposed the recruitment of foreign workers but resistance was dropped after assurances that Polish recruits would receive full union rates of pay and be the first to lose their jobs in any situation requiring redundancies.

The election of a Labour government under Prime Minister Clement Attlee in 1945 ensured that the coal industry would be nationalised, and not returned to private ownership as had happened at the end of the First World War. Under the provisions of a 1938 Coal Act, mineral rights to the

North Staffordshire Collieries in 1945

Coal Owner	Mine/s	Number of Employees				
		Below 10	11-50	51-250	250-1000	1000+
Alsagers Bank Colliery	Alsagers Bank	√				
Apedale Hall Colliery	No.1; No. 2, No. 3	√				
Baskeyfield & Son	Mitchell's Wood			√		
Berry Hill Collieries	Berry Hill (Knowles, New Top) Folly					√
Biddulph Mining	Gillow Heath	√				
Bignall Hill Colliery	Rookery				√	
W.D. Castle	The Beeches Woodstock No.3			√		
Chatterley Whitfield	Whitfield-Hesketh Middle + Winstanley Institute + Platt					√
Church Hills Colliery	Church Hills	√				
Clough Hall Colliery	No. 3, Hollingwood	√				
J. & G. Coleman	Parklands No. 1	√				
Dales Green	Red Hall		√			
Fenton Collieries	Glebe				√	
Florence Coal & Iron	No. 1, No. 2					√
Foxfield Colliery	Foxfield (Hall Park)				√	
Glasshouse Colliery	No. 1			√		
Goldenhill	Cannel Row	√				
Greenfield Collieries	Talke Green No. 5			√		
Griffiths & Burgess	Burley Lane	√				
Hayes Wood Colliery	No. 8, No. 9			√		
Holditch Mines	Holditch, New Apedale					√
I. Joynson	Podmore Hall	√				
Lowlands Colliery	Ravenscliffe			√		
H. Machin	Miry Wood	√				
Madeley Collieries	Leycett				√	
Merryhill Colliery	No. 1, No. 5				√	
Mossfield Colliery	Mossfield, Park Hall					√
Mount Colliery (J. Blood & W.H. Stone)	No. 4	√				
New High Carr Colliery	New High Carr				√	
North Midland Colliery	North Midland			√		
Norton & Biddulph Collieries	Norton, Victoria					√
Parkhouse Collieries	Parkhouse				√	
F. & E. Pepper	Hall Field No. 1, No. 2	√				
G. Platt	Woodhouse No. 1, No. 3	√				
Red Street Collieries	No. 1, No. 2			√		
A. Roberts	Heathcote Road	√				
Shelton Iron & Steel	Hanley Deep Silverdale					√
Sneyd Collieries	No. 1, No. 2, No. 4					√
Snow Hill Colliery	Snow Hill	√				
Spring Wood Colliery	Spring Wood	√				
Stafford Coal & Iron	No. 1 (Kemball, Pender, Bourne, Hem Heath) No. 2 (Sutherland, Homer)					√
Tidsley Colliery (E. Hambleton)	Tidsley	√				
Watermills Colliery	No. 4, No. 5, No. 6		√			
Wolstanton Colliery	Wolstanton				√	

Source: Ministry of Fuel and Power 'List of Mines in Great Britain and the Isle of Man' and local directories

122 *North Staffordshire collieries in 1945.*

South Staffordshire Collieries in 1945

Coal Owner	Mine/s	Below 10	11-50	51-250	250-1000	1000+
Alley Colliery	Alley, Straits	√				
Baggeridge Colliery	Baggeridge					√
Coombs Wood Collieries	Coombs Wood	√				
Ellowes Colliery (B. Williams)	Ellowes			√		
Furnace Colliery	Furnace	√				
Gibbons (Dudley)	Dibdale No. 1, No. 2, No. 3				√	
Grosvenor Colliery	No. 1			√		
J. Hall	Clay Pit, Delph			√		
Hamstead Colliery	Hamstead				√	
G. King Harrison	Hawbush No. 2			√		
London Fields Colliery	Lodge			√		
Mobberley & Perry	Mobberley & Perry				√	
E.J. & J. Pearson	Plants Hollow, Barn, Cottage, Crown, Delph				√	
J.T. Price	Saltwells			√		
J. Round	Mount Pleasant (No. 2)				√	
Shut End Colliery	Standhills					
J. Stevens	Hurst, Lower Hurst, New Drift	√				
Timmis & Co.	Amblecote Bank (No.1, No.2, No.3, No. 4, No. 5)	√				
Warwickshire Coal Co.	Sandwell Park (Jubilee)				√	

Source: Ministry of Fuel and Power 'List of Mines in Great Britain and the Isle of Man' and local directories

124 *South Stafford-shire collieries in 1945.*

Cannock Chase Collieries in 1945

Coal Owner	Mine/s	Below 10	11-50	51-250	250-1000	1000+
S. Baillie	Pool Hayes		√			
Brereton Collieries	Brereton (Brick Kiln) No. 1, No. 2 Old Engine, New Day					√
Broadway Collieries	Coppice Farm No.1, No. 2			√		
C & F Collieries	Old Wilkin		√			
Cannock & Leacroft Colliery	Cannock & Leacroft				√	
Cannock & Rugeley Colliery	Cannock Wood Wimblebury					√
Cannock Chase Colliery	No. 3, No. 7, No. 8, No. 9					√
G. Cooper	Caddick's Farm		√			
Coppice Colliery	Coppice				√	
J. & B. Cox Colliery	Pool Lane		√			
East Cannock Colliery	East Cannock				√	
Brownhills Colliery (W.H. Harrison)	Brownhills (Grove) Mid Cannock Wyrley No. 3				√	
Hilton Main & Holly Bank	Hilton Main No. 1, No. 2 Holly Bank No. 3, No. 5, No. 7, No. 15					√
Kingswood Colliery	Kingswood		√			
Littleton Collieries	Conduit No. 3, No. 4 Littleton No. 2, No. 3					√
Nook & Wyrley Collieries	Nook & Wyrley Yard Drift (No. 2)			√		
Old Coppice Colliery (T.A. Hawkins)	Cannock Old Coppice				√	
F.T. Screen	Sling	√				
Walsall Wood Colliery	Walsall Wood				√	
West Cannock Colliery	No. 1, No. 2, No. 3, No. 5 (downcast), No. 5 (upcast)					√
West Coppice Collieries (Potters Clay & Coal)	West Coppice,			√		
S.J. Whitehouse	Bulls Meadow		√			
Wilkin Colliery	Wilkin			√		
A. Wilks	Spring Meadow (No. 2)		√			

Source: Ministry of Fuel and Power 'List of Mines in Great Britain and the Isle of Man' and local directories

123 *Cannock Chase collieries in 1945.*

Staffordshire mines licensed by the National Coal Board in 1947

North Staffordshire
Alsagers Bank Colliery
Baskeyfield & Son
Biddulph Mining
A. Booth, J. Cook, G.A.
Forster
W.D. Castle
Church Hills Colliery
Clough Hall Colliery
J. & G. Coleman
W.C. Coleman
Dales Green
Greenfield Collieries
Griffiths & Burgess
Hayes Wood Colliery
Hinks & Nixon
I. Joynson
J.A. Knight
Lowlands Colliery
H. Machin

Merryhill Colliery
W.R. Midwinter
Mount Colliery
New High Carr Colliery
F. & E. Pepper
G. Platt
Red Street Collieries
Rhodes & Dumbill
A. Roberts
Snowhill Colliery
Spring Wood Colliery
Sproston Brothers
F. Taylor
Tidsley Colliery
Watermills Colliery

Cannock Chase
Broadway Colliery
C. & F. Collieries
G. Cooper

J. & B. Cox Colliery
Kingswood Colliery
West Coppice Colliery
S.J. Whitehouse
Wilkin Colliery
A. Wilks

South Staffordshire
Alley Colliery
Coombs Wood Collieries
Ellowes Colliery
Furnace Colliery
Grosvenor Colliery
J. Hall
London Fields Colliery
E.J. & J. Pearson
J.T. Price
J. Stevens

Source: Colliery Year Book and Coal Trades Directory 1947

125 *Staffordshire mines licensed by the National Coal Board in 1947.*

coal itself were already owned by the state. Negligible deposits were 'alienated', or exempt under the Act, to allow small amounts of coal to be removed if necessary for other activities, such as clay working, to continue. Small enterprises, defined as those employing fewer than 30 miners underground, were required to apply for a licence in order to carry on in private ownership. Those businesses granted licences In Staffordshire were almost exclusively opencast operations. Thirty-three licences were granted in the north of the county, the majority along the western flank of the coalfield. Ten licensed mines in South Staffordshire were concentrated around Dudley. Nine licences were issued to companies on the Cannock Chase field.

The Coal Industry Nationalisation Act passed into law on 12 July 1946. A preamble set out the government's objectives:

There shall be a National Coal Board which shall, on and after the primary vesting date, be charged with the duties of: (a) working and getting the coal in Great Britain, to the exclusion (save in this Act provided) of any other person; (b) securing the efficient development of the coalmining industry; and, (c) making supplies of coal available, of such qualities and sizes, in such quantities and such prices, as may seem to them best calculated to further the public interest in all respects, including the avoidance of any undue preference or advantage.

MIDLAND DISTRICT VALUATION BOARD									
Undertaking: THE WEST CANNOCK COLLIERY COMPANY LIMITED									1
Year Ended 31st December	1930	1931	1932	1933	1934	1935	1936	1937	1938
1. No. of persons employed*									
(a) Face	1,006	1,029	1,030	1,028	1,020	986	984	969	951
(b) Elsewhere underground	1,191	1,148	1,170	1,073	1,096	1,015	1,014	983	1,012
(c) Surface	462	515	522	528	538	542	542	572	557
(d) Total	2,659	2,692	2,722	2,629	2,654	2,543	2,540	2,524	2,520
2. Output of Coal									
(a) Pithead Weight	508,086	550,101	525,958	505,377	559,505	578,862	602,935	625,431	600,433
(b) Saleable Coal	514,722	563,836	540,408	524,407	581,249	612,429	648,522	689,055	660,145
(c) (b) as % of (a)	101·3	102·5	102·7	103·8	103·9	105·8	107·6	110·2	109·9
(d) Tons S.C. per person per ann.	194	209	199	199	219	241	255	273	262
3. Colliery Consumption (tons)	25,803	25,464	26,261	24,972	27,085	27,729	30,442	32,728	32,727
4. Miners' Coal (tons)	15,230	15,512	15,311	14,821	15,105	15,078	15,202	16,043	15,634
5. Coal Commercially Disposable (tons)									
(a) Domestic				Information not available					324,015
(b) Industrial				do.	do.				
(i) Supplied to excluded works				do.	do.				
(ii) Other supplies				do.	do.				
(iii) Total				do.	do.				287,769
(c) Total Domestic and Industrial	473,689	522,860	488,836	484,614	539,059	569,622	602,878	640,284	611,784

* The average of men actually at work

126   *Extract from the Midland District Valuation Board Inspector's Report on West Cannock Colliery recording numbers employed and output in the period 1930-8.*

On the morning of 1 January 1947, notices were posted at every pit declaring:

This Colliery is now managed by the National Coal Board on behalf of the People.

Despite reference to 'efficient development', it is clear the key aim was to run the National Coal Board as a public service in the public interest and not as a purely commercial enterprise. Lord Hyndley was appointed as the first chairman of the NCB and announced his intention of raising 200 million tons of coal a year, based on estimated reserves of 20,000,000,000 tons.

The situation he inherited was one of decline. Export trade lost during the strike of 1926 had never been regained. Subsidised mines in Germany and Poland had taken advantage of the opportunity to penetrate valuable overseas markets in Scandinavia and elsewhere. International protectionism, perhaps most significantly import restrictions imposed by France and Spain in the interwar years, had compounded problems. Statutory regulation of output introduced by the 1930 Coal Mines Act and price controls at district level had only served to intensify domestic competition, and government intervention designed to force colliery owners to amalgamate in the interests of efficiency had been constrained by fear of exacerbating the problem of high

WEST CANNOCK COLLIERY CO. LTD.

COAL RESERVES FROM 1ST JANUARY 1947

DISTRICT NAME OF SEAM	DEPTH IN FEET	COLLIERY NAME OF SEAM	AVER. THICK FT INS		ACRES	TONS WORKABLE
OLD MANS	82	SEVEN FEET	2	4	734	2 055 200
BROOCH	108	BROOCH	4	1	886	4 341 400
BENCHES	226	FIVE FEET	5	3	841	5 247 094
EIGHT FEET	265	TOP HARD	4	6	686	3 704 400
OLD PARK	372	MAIN HARD	5	0	763	4 578 000
HEATHEN	534	HATHERTON MAIN	4	0	872	4 138 688
SULPHUR	624	HEATHEN	4	4	1921	9 989 200
YARD	661	YARD	2	6	2073	6 385 128
BASS	733	SIX FEET	3	4	2042	8 152 168
NEWMINE	810	TOP SHALLOW	4	6	2631	12 722 674
SHALLOW	824	SHALLOW	6	0	1382	8 634 230
TOP DEEP	855	TOP DEEP	3	6	2509	10 537 740
DEEP	929	DEEP	6	0	214	1 386 720 } 7,476,188.
			3	6	1612	6 089 468 }
						87,968,110

FIGURES CALCULATED AT 1200 TONS PER FOOT ACRE AND A 10% ALLOWANCE FOR MINOR FAULTS TO A 60 YARDS COVER LINE TO BASE OF TRIAS.

127 *Coal resources at West Cannock Colliery recorded by the Midland District Valuation Board Inspector under the regulations of the Coal Industry Act. At the time of vesting, in 1946, calculations showed reserves in excess of 87 million tons, a figure that gave an estimated colliery life of 130 years.*

unemployment. Productivity at national level was steadily falling year on year, although that trend had been reversed in Staffordshire in the twelve months following the end of the war.

Primary vesting day was set for 1 January 1947. Despite much talk of nationalisation since Keir Hardie first seriously proposed it in 1893, little practical thought had been given to the exercise. This left a huge amount to be accomplished in just five months in order to put in place an administrative structure that would ensure continuity and a smooth handover. The creation of the NCB made it the largest industrial employer in the world outside the Communist bloc. District Valuation Boards were set up to collect information on operating assets in order to agree compensation payments. Where colliery companies were continuing in business in other areas, for example those involved in iron and steel manufacture, this meant disaggregating mining from other activities. Inspectors visited each colliery to gather information under a range of headings and collate supporting documentary evidence. Detailed plans showing the seams worked and an analysis of reserves were drawn up. Employee lists were checked, and an inventory of all plant, equipment and other physical assets compiled. With a

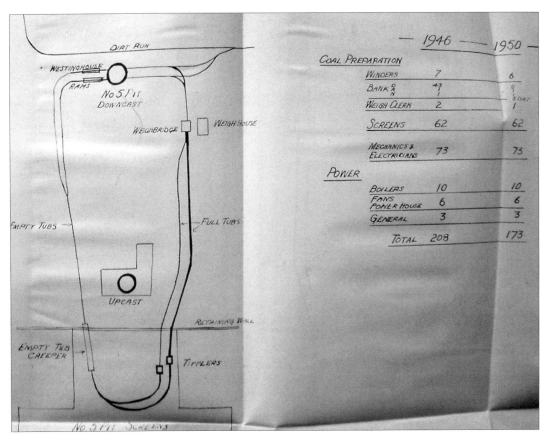

128   *Sketch plan of West Cannock No. 4 Pit, 1950.*

fixed sum available for allocation, private colliery owners were in competition for compensation. In many cases assessment was disputed. It was 1955 before most of the outstanding claims were settled.

Eight Divisional Boards were established by the NCB. West Midlands (No. 6 Division), covering Staffordshire, Shropshire and Warwickshire, acquired Himley Hall, former home of the Earls of Dudley, as its headquarters. Sir Ben Smith became Division Chairman. I.W. Cumberbatch (North Staffordshire), R. Bennett (Cannock Chase), and J. Dando (South Staffordshire) were appointed General Managers in individual area coalfields. Faced with rationalisation,

change and uncertainty, many senior colliery staff chose not to transfer to the NCB, leaving the new Board with a shortage of experienced managers and compounding the problems of an overall manpower shortage and declining productivity.

At the time of nationalisation there were 20 mines in North Staffordshire employing 14,861 underground and 5,364 on the surface: Apedale, Berry Hill, Chatterley Whitfield, Fenton (Glebe), Florence, Foxfield, Glasshouse, Hanley Deep, Hem Heath, Holditch, Madeley (Leycett), Mossfield, Norton, Parkhall, Parkhouse, Silverdale, Sneyd, Stafford (No. 1 Pit and No. 2 Pit), Victoria and Wolstanton. In the

Cannock Chase area, 12,464 underground and 4,957 surface workers were employed at: Brereton, Cannock Chase (No. 3 Pit, No. 8 Pit and No. 9 Pit), Cannock Wood, Wimblebury, East Cannock, Littleton, including the Conduit Pits retained by Littleton after their takeover of the Conduit Colliery Company in 1931, West Cannock (No. 1 Pit, No. 2 Pit, No. 3 Pit and No. 5 'Tackeroo' Pit), Cannock and Leacroft, Coppice, Grove, Mid Cannock, Wyrley No. 3 Pit, Cannock Old Coppice (later renamed 'Hawkins'), Hilton Main (including Holly Bank), Nook and Wyrley, and Walsall Wood. In the South Staffordshire field nationalisation affected 3,926 underground and 1,211 surface employees, a number that included workers at Mobberley and Perry (from 1958 part of Beech Tree Colliery, Colley Gate, Cradley), Shut End, Kingswinford,

Hamstead, Sandwell Park (Jubilee Pit) and Baggeridge.

After reviewing reserves and capacity, West Midlands Regional Board planned to reduce the overall total to between 16 and 18 large modernised mines, with reconstructed pit groupings around a central unit. East Cannock Colliery was among the first to be affected. In 1948 the Top Robins seam was considered uneconomic for continued working. Although all 122 men employed at the pit were transferred, it triggered concerns about possible job losses at the same time as recruitment was being stepped up. New houses and roads built to cope with a flood of miners attracted to work in the Cannock Chase coalfield created what was virtually a new town out of the villages of Burntwood, Chasetown and Chase Terrace, where the population shot from 10,000 to 50,000 almost overnight.

130 *Lamps on charge in the new lamphouse installed at Walsall Wood Colliery after nationalisation.*

With such high expectations of nationalisation, some disillusionment with the new regime was predictable. At a public meeting in Hednesford, collier and former miners' agent Robert Condon criticised the bureaucracy of the NCB:

> All that has happened is that the mining industry has been turned into a vast state monopoly … miners see tendencies to increase the workers' burden instead of modernising the industry.

A prolonged and severe cold spell at the beginning of 1947 put immediate pressure on coal supplies. With factories contemplating the necessity of short-time working, the government lifted the import duty on oil, imposed to protect the domestic coal industry during the trade depression in 1934. A standard

five-day week had been introduced with nationalisation. Miners on Cannock Chase held an impromptu meeting and agreed to work Sundays to help alleviate shortages and maintain the market share of coal. Community volunteers turned up to give support by helping with surface duties and the railways cleared lines of other traffic to ensure distribution.

The new West Midlands Regional Coal Board response was to issue a notice banning further Sunday working, a ruling promptly overturned by Emmanuel Shinwell, Minister of Fuel and Power. This was a decision the pre-nationalisation chairman of Cannock Associated Collieries, W.H. Harrison, was swift to criticise:

> It passes comprehension how Mr Shinwell, sitting in London far away from the scene of operations, can

pretend to pass judgment on local officials, who make a daily study of every circumstance.

In an effort to increase production the NCB and NUM agreed to extend working time from autumn 1947. Staffordshire's miners voted for an extra shift on Saturday, rather than lengthened shift times, subject to agreement that working Saturdays did not clash with the home fixtures of local football teams. A promising start was made on the first few additional shifts but attendance soon dwindled. Impact on overall output was negligible and the experiment was abandoned. Voluntary Saturday shifts recommenced in February 1963 to cope with another long-lasting cold snap.

Working conditions improved with nationalisation. A comprehensive Mines and Quarries Act (1954) implemented a clutch of health and welfare recommendations made by previous Royal Commissions. It was the first Act of Parliament to deal with safety measures in a considered, objective way rather than in the wake of some disaster. New Rescue Stations were established at Berry Hill and Hednesford. A medical service was introduced. Canteens and pithead showers were installed as a priority at those mines lacking facilities. Where the life of a colliery was not assured beyond 15 years, prefabricated shower units were installed. The first of these in Staffordshire was put in at Yew Tree drift mine, Essington. The Coal Industry Social Welfare Organisation (CISWO) superseded the Miners' Welfare Commission in 1952. Operating through area committees and full-time officers, it ensured all collieries had access to welfare institutes, sports facilities and social amenities.

Cannock Chase became the first coalfield in Western Division to centralise maintenance work. One hundred and fifty mechanics, electricians and other tradesmen moved to workshops at Cannock Chase Colliery's No. 3 Pit in 1955, from where they covered the whole of Cannock Chase and South Staffordshire.

In November 1956 an influx of Hungarian refugees fleeing the Soviet offensive in their homeland offered a potential source of new manpower. Thirteen hundred, housed in hostels at Knutton in North Staffordshire and Bridgtown near Cannock, received crash courses in English and basic mining skills training in the early months of 1957. Despite assurances from the West Midlands Regional Board of future job security linked to expansion – there were even long-term plans to link Cannock Chase with the South Derbyshire coalfield at Cadley Hill Colliery, Church Gresley – recruitment met with resistance from the NUM, who feared the programme of consolidation then under way carried the threat of redundancies. Littleton Colliery's Conduit No. 3 Pit and No. 4 Pit, Nook and Wyrley, and West Cannock No. 3 Pit all closed in 1949, soon after nationalisation, and mergers at Cannock Chase Colliery left just No. 3 and No. 8 Pits operational by 1951. Hilton Main shut down Holly Bank in 1952, and in the same year Grove merged with Wyrley No. 3 Pit. At a number of mines reserves were approaching exhaustion. To maximise the available 'take' and economise on surface operations, Cannock and Leacroft fused with Mid Cannock in 1954, West Cannock No. 2 Pit was combined with West Cannock No. 5 Pit in 1956, and two years later West Cannock No. 1 Pit was connected by a heading to Littleton. Mining ceased at East Cannock in 1957. Closures followed at Cannock Chase No. 3 Pit (1959), Brereton (1960), Cannock Chase No. 8 Pit (1962), Hawkins (Old Coppice Pit) (1964), Walsall Wood (1964) and Mid Cannock (1967). Wimblebury was networked into West Cannock

131   *One of the last pit ponies at Baggeridge Colliery. Eight ponies aged between 13 and 20 remained when production ended in 1967. All were found homes, two of them with former keeper Harold Worton.*

No. 5 in 1962, and in 1963 a 1,200-yard underground link was driven between Wyrley No. 3 and Mid Cannock.

Similar reconfiguration took place in the rest of the county. Sandwell Park closed in 1960. Geological problems hastened the closure of Hamstead Colliery in 1965. Baggeridge Colliery, the last working mine in South Staffordshire, was declared uneconomic and production ended in 1967. After salvage operations the pit was closed the following year.

In North Staffordshire exhaustion of economic reserves closed Madeley (1957), Glasshouse (1960), Berry Hill (1960), Parkhall (merged with Florence in 1962), Mossfield (1963), Fenton (1964) and Foxfield (1965). Flooding hastened the closure of Parkhouse in 1968. In 1967 the West Midlands Division was reorganised. Staffordshire became part of a new South Midlands area grouping. Twenty years after nationalisation, linkages, mergers and a strong focus on the most productive pits left the county with just 15 operational mines: five on Cannock Chase and 10 in North Staffordshire. With picks and shovels vanishing into history and pit bottoms re-organised to accommodate locomotives and mine cars, Staffordshire was producing significantly more coal than before the NCB took over and consistently topped the productivity league. In a further round of consolidation in 1969 both Apedale and Stafford collieries closed. Apedale, the only remaining drift mine in Staffordshire, re-opened two years later as a licensed mine under private ownership and continued small-scale production until 1999.

A new colliery was built at Hem Heath and a 24ft diameter coal-winding shaft sunk, with distinctively shaped headgear known

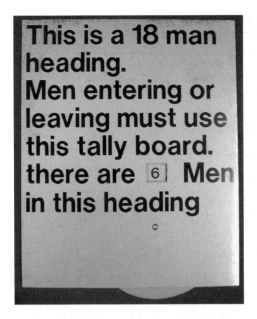

This is a 18 man heading.
Men entering or leaving must use this tally board.
there are 6 Men in this heading

132 *Tally board for the number of men at a heading, the inset wheel adjusted as men entered or left.*

locally as the 'Big A'. Annual output reached the magic one million tons figure at Hem Heath in 1966. Wolstanton, the deepest pit in western Europe at 3,750 feet, had passed the one million tons a year output figure in 1963. An allocation of £10 million was made for a complete overhaul and complicated underground merger with Hanley Deep and Sneyd. In 1969 the upper strata of general purpose coal was abandoned in order to concentrate on deeper seams of carbonising coal, for which a more secure market was envisaged. A third 'dip' roadway was driven at Holditch and a fourth planned.

Staffordshire was at the forefront of research and development. A technique known as 'retreat longwall' emerged for working the steeply inclined seams of North Staffordshire. Driving roadways before coal was extracted required precise

133 *Huwood Mastabar 4/250 ton powered supports in 7ft 6in. extraction.*

134 *Manriding conveyor, Cannock Chase.*

135 *Chainless shearing with heavy duty supports in place at Littleton Colliery.*

136   *Winding engine house, Lea Hall Colliery.*

forward planning to bring faces on line to schedule, but was a much simpler method than conventional advance longwall mining, with its necessarily complicated face end arrangements. Cutting individual faces homewards from a heading driven to the dip lowered the risk of spontaneous combustion and allowed gravity to assist the return of full tubs. Earlier research at Stafford Colliery had shown how methane could be piped to the surface and put to practical use, producing financial benefits and making deep mines considerably safer. At Silverdale Colliery, where the system was first tried using the latest heavy-duty machinery, a European driving record of 136 yards in a week was set in 1967.

Chatterley Whitfield became the first UK colliery to computerise its payroll. On the Cannock Chase field, Cannock Wood, Hilton Main, Mid Cannock and Littleton collieries were the main beneficiaries of investment in modernisation. Valley Colliery closed in 1962 and was developed as a training centre. Electric winding engines replaced steam plant. Surface installations were renovated or replaced, preparation plant updated, pit bottoms rebuilt. Over £3 million was set aside for reconstruction at Littleton and Hilton Main. Deep 'horizon' roads (level main roads suitable for locomotives) enabled two-and-a-half ton mine cars to replace endless rope systems hauling 12cwt capacity tubs. Coal from upper seams was delivered to the loco roads for loading via spiral chutes. In 1964 Littleton was the first colliery in the UK to have closed circuit television installed.

Plans for the NCB's first totally new mining venture, to supply an electricity generating power station on a shared Trentside site at Rugeley, were announced in 1951. Work started at Lea Hall Farm

137   *Dint header at Lea Hall Colliery, used for cutting roadways.*

in 1954. The low-lying river valley site presented a number of engineering challenges. In order to construct two concrete-lined 24ft diameter shafts through the water-bearing strata, the ground was frozen to a depth of over 220 yards. Designed for horizon mining, working faces were connected by chutes to haulage roads. Battery-powered locomotives hauled three-ton capacity cars. A direct conveyor supplied the adjoining power station with the best quality coal reserved for domestic consumption. Production at Lea Hall began in 1960, the year Brereton Colliery closed. Many miners transferred to Lea Hall. Moving from pit to pit became a common experience. When Hilton Main shut down in 1969, after experiencing a catalogue of geological problems just five years after being designated a 'long-life pit', one of the miners affected, who had moved five times since coming to

Staffordshire from Durham, complained, 'We are just like so many cattle, herded from one colliery to another.' Most of the men from Hilton Main transferred to Littleton or West Cannock.

Lea Hall Colliery passed the milestone of one million tons a year in 1963, set a UK record of one and a half million tons per annum in 1965, and smashed this landmark in 1975, reaching 1,789,681 tons in a calendar year. In 1970 the NCB made a loss but Staffordshire showed a clear profit. Output per manpower shift averaged 50.5 cwt compared to only 43.4 cwt nationally, making Staffordshire the second most profitable area. During the year, Silverdale Colliery had set a new national output per manpower shift record, breaking a previous best by neighbouring Apedale. At one point, output at Silverdale reached nine times the national average, an incredible production rate that put coal on

138   *Disc shearer in operation at Lea Hall Colliery, with hydraulic props supporting the roof.*

139   *Miners celebrate production of one and a half million tons in a calendar year at Lea Hall Colliery on 20 December 1965, surrounded by Christmas food hampers.*

an equivalent cost per therm with natural gas. Around 80 per cent of Staffordshire's output was sold in the Midlands. The rest went to customers in mid and north Wales, the north west of England and Northern Ireland. Electricity generating stations were the largest consumers.

Determined efforts by the NCB to open up export markets for British Coal met with only limited success. Short-term contracts were agreed with various European countries, Belgium, Sweden, Denmark and Romania among them. There was no significant penetration of international markets and by now domestic consumption was in freefall. Homes and power stations were being converted to natural gas. Vast reserves of North Sea oil were tapped. There was competition from cheap imported coal and from nuclear energy. In 1969 authorities in Tamworth, a town selected for expansion as part of a Birmingham 'overspill' scheme with a forward building programme of 1,000 houses a year, delivered a snub to local miners by concluding a 20 year deal for oil-fired heating as standard.

Production dominated NCB policy. Optimum output from a minimum number of faces was the aim. A so-called 'jeopardy list' was drawn up of under-performing or uneconomic collieries. Holditch and Wolstanton earned a reprieve with an improvement in productivity, but Cannock Wood closed down in 1973. Further structural reorganisation put Staffordshire in a newly formed Western Area from 1 April 1974. Former Director of Staffordshire, Ray Hunter, took over as head of the new division, managing an area stretching from Staffordshire to the Scottish Border from headquarters in Stoke-on-Trent. Despite all too apparent challenges, including the rise of energy conservation up the political agenda, stricter environmental regulations, and

an inability to compete in international markets, a prosperous future based on an ambitious expansion strategy was set out in a new, upbeat *Plan for Coal* published in 1974.

A price hike announced by Sir Derek Ezra, NCB Chairman, on a visit to Littleton Colliery in 1975 damaged prospects of competitively pricing domestic coal in the wider energy market. The rise was partly necessary to cover the cost of a recent pay settlement that had increased differentials between underground and surface workers and introduced a bonus scheme linked to productivity. The increase was also intended to be a step towards phasing out coal's long-term dependence on government subsidy. In retrospect, it sounded a warning note. For the moment it was all systems go. Every colliery was required to produce an Action Programme as part of yearly plans. Output per manshift (OMS) was the mantra. Performance figures for each pit were centrally monitored against projected targets.

Staffordshire's record, coupled with vast reserves of coal suitable for producing gas and high-grade steel, led to further investment. Modernisation programmes focused on the drive for productivity. Cost was a secondary consideration. Cantilevered supports with hydraulic props, and 'chocks' incorporating adjustable twin beams with two or more hydraulic legs mounted on a self-advancing steel platform, replaced traditional pit props. Remote control and monitoring equipment was introduced. Where there was sufficient room at the face, powerful cutter loaders – ploughs, trepanners and shearers – superseded hand-held cutters, but coalface machinery was constrained by haulage limitations. Without widening and straightening, many roadways were unable to accommodate the conveyors, locomotives and mine cars necessary for maximum efficiency.

Sir Derek Ezra announced a £20 million project to develop the potential of Silverdale on a visit to the colliery in October 1976. Work began soon afterwards to extend an existing drift and drive two additional surface drifts into new areas. The same year, in response to stricter environmental controls, Silverdale installed a groundbreaking water treatment plant that attracted worldwide interest. The revolutionary system actively filtered mine water at a rate of 400 gallons a minute, removing the need for large settling lagoons and enabling clean water to be pumped directly into the River Trent.

A budget of £7 million was assigned to reconstruct Florence Colliery. Coal from Chatterley Whitfield had been raised at Wolstanton since the completion of an underground link in January 1976. In 1977 a full merger took place, and Chatterley Whitfield closed. Conveyor systems were upgraded to cope with increased output.

Manriding trains and conveyors cut down travelling time to the face. Productivity records were being set on an almost weekly basis in Staffordshire's pits. Silverdale set new European records for both face productivity and tunnel driving. In his speech at Silverdale in 1976 Sir Derek Ezra outlined national targets for the industry of 200 million tons a year by the millennium.

Proposals for a full countywide geological exploration programme were approved. Littleton and Lea Hall were both earmarked for further investment. There were ambitious plans for the future development of North Staffordshire's operational pits. A recruitment drive was launched to attract trainee miners. 'Come and join us' trumpeted the NCB in a booklet aimed at school leavers entitled *Mining's Big in Staffordshire*. Former miners received letters inviting them to return to the industry. Mobile recruiting offices toured the county.

140 (opposite) *Man-riding train, Hem Heath Colliery, 1970. Man-riding cut down travelling time to the face.*

141 (right) *The second new drift at Hem Heath/Trentham 'Superpit', completed in 1981.*

There were setbacks. An inrush of water at West Cannock No. 5 Pit in 1976 had forced the main Park seam face to be abandoned. The seventy men affected were transferred to Littleton. Norton Colliery, Ford Green closed in 1977. But there were also success stories. Within three years of losing one coalface, West Cannock Colliery was setting productivity records using retreat mining and advance technology on one of two remaining operational faces.

The Trentham Project, a £30 million scheme to merge Florence and Hem Heath in a new 'superpit', was announced. The first two and a quarter mile roadway was completed with inch-perfect accuracy in 1979. A second followed in 1981 and Councillor Mrs Mary Stringer, Lord Mayor of Stoke-on-Trent, officially declared the new integrated colliery complex open. Trentham was equipped with the latest technology. Anderson-Mavor heavy-duty power loaders and Braun Type EKF3 single strand conveyors were installed. A trough-profile cable belt system capable of carrying more than conventional conveyors of the same overall (42in.) width, the first of its type in NCB's Western Area, could handle 800 tons per hour. Methane was pumped to the surface and used to generate steam. Surplus gas was sold. Manriding was by locomotive-hauled trains. Beneath its 'A' frame headgear, the 24ft diameter No. 2 downcast shaft was used for coal winding and end-of-shift manriding. Four cages operated in tandem, each pair with its own winding engine. The smaller (19ft 6in. diameter) No. 1 shaft providing upcast ventilation was used for materials, salvage and inshift manriding.

In 1982 it was agreed that workable reserves in the Ten Feet seam at Victoria Colliery were nearing exhaustion and that when the existing face was worked out the pit would close and the men be offered

142   *Rapid loader system in operation at Littleton Colliery. Diesel locomotives hauled loaded trucks to sidings at Penkridge for onward distribution.*

transfers to Trentham (Hem Heath) or Holditch. West Cannock No. 5 Pit closed the same year.

Technology allowed an increasing level of remote working and as a consequence the industry became less labour-intensive. Investment in heavy-duty machinery continued. Anderson Strathclyde drum shearers, both single- and double-ended, were a popular choice in Staffordshire. New techniques of strata control and roof bolting improved roadways. A £5 million scheme furnished Holditch with electric winding engines in 1981 and enabled skip winding in one shaft. A new coal preparation plant at the colliery was capable of washing and blending 1,000 tons of coal hourly. Discharge was via a

rapid loading system direct to rail wagons for delivery to the power stations of the Trent Valley and north-western England.

Much of the 1974 *Plan for Coal* strategy was based on an assumption of limitless supplies of fuel from all primary sources and continuing growth in demand, a valid enough prospectus when coal was still the nation's main supplier of energy and demand was high. But it failed to envisage falling demand. When market realities began to take over there was no 'Plan B'. Research and capital had been devoted to ambitious projects that never left the drawing board. In 1979 a planning application was lodged with Stafford Borough Council for a new superpit on a site off Within Lane, between the villages of Hopton and Salt. Park New Mine was expected to employ a workforce of 1,400 and produce in excess of two million tons of coal a year from ten or more workable seams on a northern extension of the Cannock Chase coalfield.

In 1983 Ian MacGregor was appointed to succeed Sir Derek Ezra as NCB chairman. MacGregor had earned the nickname 'Mac the Knife' after presiding over swingeing closures in the steel industry. Faced with growing pessimism about the future of the industry, MacGregor made an effort to raise morale. Soon after his appointment he paid a visit to Lea Hall Colliery, and after more than two hours spent underground declared it 'one of the best pits in the world'.

The damaging strike of 1984-5 exposed deep underlying economic problems and the inadequacy of the 1974 strategy. After nearly four decades of nationalisation and £5.6 billion of public money the NCB was bankrupt. Continuing decline in demand and inability to compete internationally forced more closures. Wolstanton wound its last coal in 1985. Programmes were introduced to offset the

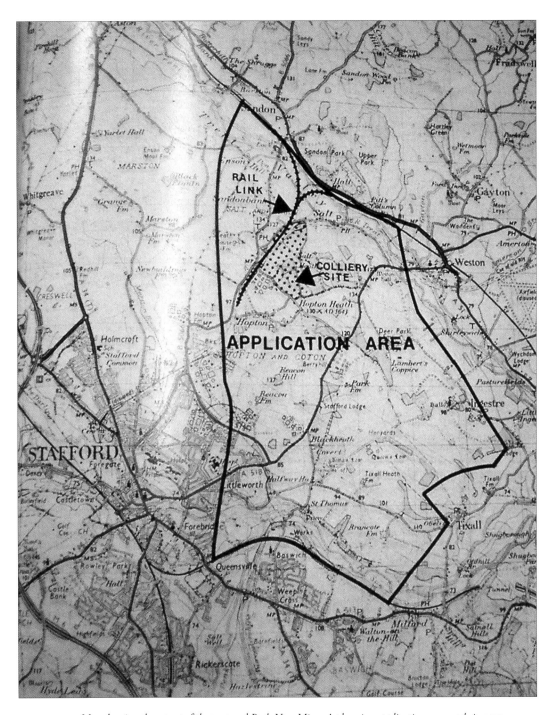

143 *Map showing the extent of the proposed Park New Mine. A planning application was made in 1979.*

144   *Enterprise Centre set up at West Cannock No. 5 Pit beside the former canteen and shower block. The pithead wheel was rescued from Holditch Colliery.*

145   *Toasting the one million ton production landmark achieved at Littleton Colliery in 1986-7.*

fallout from necessary restructuring and job losses. NCB Enterprise (later British Coal Enterprise) was set up to spearhead attempts to create new job opportunities in and around coalfields. A Job and Career Change Scheme (JACCS) was introduced. Practical advice and financial assistance was available to launch new small businesses and help existing businesses to expand. Attracting secondees from industry contained the cost of providing programmes. Although primarily aimed at helping redundant miners, there was little enthusiasm for retraining among those with long service. BCE's wider remit embraced creating opportunities for a new generation of young people in coalfield areas whose expectations of possible careers in the coal industry had disappeared.

In 1986 a shake-up of the NCB resulted in a new administrative body, British Coal Corporation (BCC). Production goals were replaced with financial targets. By 1987 Western Area, with Staffordshire leading the way, was making an operating profit. Constant restructuring took place, each reorganisation fuelling rumours of job losses and adversely affecting morale. In 1987 Lea Hall and Littleton became part of a Central Area covering the South Midlands and North Derbyshire. In 1989 four English coalfield groups were created and all of Staffordshire's pits placed in a new North Western region. Consolidation measures to reduce costs followed. Holditch closed in 1989 and the Florence shaft still in use at Trentham in 1990. Mining at Lea Hall also ended in 1990.

Many of the UK's coal-fired power stations had been decommissioned or were coming to the end of their working lives by the early 1990s. Cheap imports and more rigorous European Commission regulations on nitrogen dioxide and sulphur dioxide emissions from power stations added to the pressures facing domestic mining. There was some investment in research in clean coal technology but it was too little and too late. In an increasingly competitive energy market the choice for the government was whether to continue subsidising a rising industry deficit or to pull the plug. In March 1992 President of the Board of Trade Michael Heseltine announced a programme of closures with the promise of a cash injection for retraining and regeneration for the communities affected. NUM President Arthur Scargill described the government's proposals as 'a brutal act of vandalism'. At the beginning of 1993 North Staffordshire Miners' Wives Action Group set up camp outside the gates at Trentham to draw attention to the impact closure was likely to have on the local community. Later that year three members evaded tight security to chain themselves to pithead railings close to No. 1 shaft. But this time there would be no stoppage. With reduced demand for coal there was no bargaining power.

It was expected that the mines identified as 'core pits' in British Coal's strategic plan were secure. Staffordshire's remaining miners continued to break productivity records. North Staffordshire's collieries were national productivity champions. In January 1993 the miners of Littleton toasted the colliery's fastest ever one million tons with champagne, a feat that was 'a major tribute to the commitment of the miners who work at this colliery', according to pit manager Robin Dean. Yet, by the end of the year British Coal was reporting a loss of £2.8 million in the previous six months at Huntington Pit and announced their intention to close both Littleton and Silverdale. Littleton was first in line. A formal review process would have extended the life of the mine by a few months, but in a pithead ballot despondent miners voted to forego the delay and accept closure. It was a decision tinged with profound disappointment. There was suspicion that Littleton had been sacrificed to keep two UDM pits in Nottinghamshire open. Jim Perry, Branch Secretary of the NUM, commented, 'There is a lot of bitterness here. We were one of the company's core pits and we are the first core pit to shut.' On 10 December 1993 work at Littleton ceased. A lone piper played a lament for the last deep mine on Cannock Chase and 300 miners marched in a sombre procession into Cannock town centre. Eight hundred and fifty men and their families faced a bleak Christmas.

A Coal Industry Act passed in 1994 set the scene for returning what was left of the nation's coal industry into private hands, creating a new Coal Authority as a separate licensing and supervisory body. In a pre-qualifying round of submissions, intended to identify organisations with suitable resource and capacity, RJB Mining (later renamed UK Coal) emerged as the preferred bidder for BCC's mining assets in England. A top bid at the subsequent auction clinched the deal. Hem Heath ('Trentham' had never caught on locally, and the new operators reverted to the old name) and Silverdale were leased on a 15 year term to Coal Investments plc. Significant investment followed. £5.5 million was spent on Hem Heath. An updated form of bord and pillar working was employed using two Joy 12CM15 continuous miners, each capable of cutting 120 tons per hour, twice the output from conventional longwall techniques, with two feeder/breakers connecting the face and outbye conveyor and four shuttle cars in operation. Seams worked were the Ten Feet, Hams and part of the Rough Seven Feet, each producing high quality low-sulphur coal suitable for household and a wide range of industrial uses.

Coal Investments operated with a lean management structure and multi-tasking in the workforce of just 156 compared to over 1,300 employed by BCC. Wages were below those paid to miners before privatisation but with the potential for earnings to be supplemented by a profit sharing scheme. The company soon ran into difficulty. The problem was not lack of coal but sufficient capitalisation to ride out market downturns in a difficult economic climate. Tight finances left the company vulnerable to any interruption in cash flow. Hiccups in production caused by faulting proved disastrous and Coal Investments collapsed spectacularly under a mountain of debt in 1996. Hem Heath closed. The familiar 'Big A' headgear that was such a distinctive feature of the local skyline was demolished using explosives the following year.

Former Coal Investments production superintendent Jim Sorbie acquired Silverdale from the administrators in a management buy-out and formed Midland Mining. Geological problems and soaring costs defeated the new operator also, and the reprieve turned out to be temporary. Closure in December 1998 ended seven centuries of continuous, industrial-scale deep mining in Staffordshire, a period that witnessed transition from domestic cottage industry, via structured employment in small private collectives and the advent of powerful entrepreneurial coalmasters, to nationalisation under the authority of the National Coal Board in 1947 before time ran out.

It is easy to be wise in retrospect. No one foresaw the dramatic decline of a once precious industry. But, as it took place, small groups of dedicated people set about rescuing and preserving our mining heritage before it was too late. The Black Country Living Museum, recreating the Black Country's industrial past, opened in 1975 on a 26-acre former colliery site. Chatterley Whitfield was reborn as

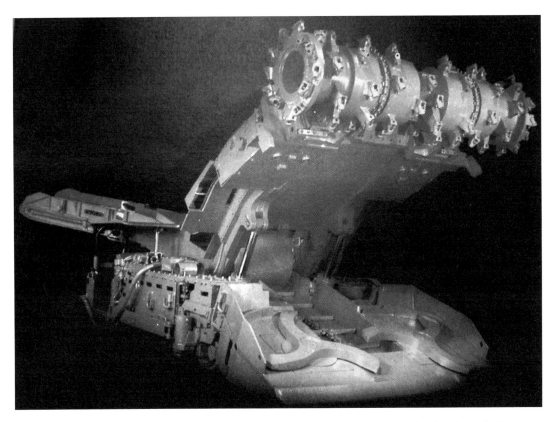

146 *Joy12CM15 continuous miner, one of a pair introduced at Hem Heath Colliery after the takeover by Coal Investments plc in 1994.*

147 *The 'Big A' headframe at Hem Heath, demolished in 1997.*

148   *Semi-derelict Guibal fan house and winding engine house of New Hawne Colliery. On either side of the central arch of the engine house, through which the winding ropes passed, are the initials of the New British Iron Company and 1865, the date the engine house was built. The fan house was added a few years later.*

the county's first underground mining museum. In 1982 it was voted Britain's best industrial museum. In March 1986 two miners using traditional hand tools cut coal from the Holly Lane seam. Darkie the pony hauled full tubs to the pit bottom, from where the coal was raised and delivered to senior citizens in Ball Green and Fegg Hayes by horse and cart.

A few years later the museum ran into financial trouble and was forced into receivership, but the Friends of Chatterley Whitfield Society remains active. Work began in 2005 to landscape the derelict site, a Scheduled Ancient Monument containing 34 buildings that together make up the most complete colliery complex in the country. 'Listing' of individual buildings and 'scheduling' of sites affords a degree of protection to a dwindling cluster of surviving structures,

but unless imaginative and sensitive uses can be found to give them purpose decline and decay is inevitable.

A rare and fascinating collection of buildings, including an almost complete Guibal fan house, steam winding engine house, stables, workshops and offices, remain of the former New Hawne Colliery. Yard and offices provided a depot for Halesowen Council's Highways Department after the colliery closed in the 1920s. Now the place is abandoned and semi-derelict. The huge area once worked by the drift mine at Apedale, now back in small-scale production supplying coal for steam trains on the East Lancashire Railway, is a country park and heritage centre. A corn store at Valley Pit, where feed for the pit ponies was once kept, has been transformed into the Museum of Cannock Chase.

149 *Pithead wheel and mine tub erected on a high point of Apedale Country Park to commemorate the coalminers of Staffordshire.*

Across the county, colliery sites have been reclaimed, raw pitheads landscaped and spoil heaps softened by grass. In their place are industrial estates, enterprise parks, houses, shopping centres, nature reserves and leisure facilities. In the early 1980s, when opencast mining returned to the site of Holly Bank Colliery, local councillor Rex Roberts declared, 'This is going to rape the village of Essington for the next ten years.' Now the site is a golf course, lush and green. Two years after Baggeridge Colliery closed, South Staffordshire Council acquired the site and created Baggeridge Country Park, opened by HRH Princess Anne in 1983. Hanley Deep Pit sleeps beneath Hanley Forest Park; the spoil heaps once nicknamed the 'Three Ugly Sisters' reduced to two grassy mounds. Britannia Stadium,

home of Stoke City Football Club, occupies the site of Stafford Colliery. A proposal to regenerate and develop the site of Silverdale Colliery was unveiled by English Partnerships after consultation with local residents in February 2006. A new village square, leafy walkways, affordable housing and a series of play areas are among the key elements envisaged.

In May 2006 a 30ft tall sculpture of a miner by artist John McKenna, jointly funded by Walsall Borough Strategic Partnership and Walsall Council, was erected at the junction of High Street and Pelsall Road, Brownhills. Finished in stainless steel and weighing five tons, the Brownhills Miner stands arms aloft, brandishing his lamp and pick in celebration of the area's long involvement with coal. An 8ft tall

Davy lamp was unveiled in Market Street, Hednesford in July 2006 as a memorial to the miners who gave their lives in service on the Cannock Chase coalfield. The names of many of those remembered are engraved on individual bricks in a surrounding wall.

By the millennium, the coal industry of Staffordshire had become submerged, the waters of time closing over it with barely a ripple. Generations of the same families earned their living in the industry. Inherent risks meant few were untouched by tragedy. Social costs went beyond miners and their families to affect whole communities. There was pride too, pride in a tough job well done. Above all there was comradeship and shared values. Memories glitter, sharp and bright as the coal once won. Deep below Staffordshire, millions of tons of coal reserves lie untouched. It will still be there long after oil and natural gas have gone.

150   *Giant sculpture of a miner by artist John McKenna erected at Brownhills in 2006.*

151   *Memorial for the miners of Cannock Chase in Market Street, Hednesford, unveiled on 30 July 2006. Bricks in a surrounding wall bear the names of individual miners.*

Sources and Further Reading

Main Sources

Allen, G.C., *The Industrial Development of Birmingham and the Black Country 1866-1927* (1929)

Aris's Birmingham Gazette (various years)

Ashworth, W. with Pegg, J., *The British Coalmining Industry* (1977)

Benson, J., 'The thrift of English coal-miners, 1860-95', *Economic History Review* (1978)

Burritt, E., *Walks in the Black Country and its Green Border-Land* (1868)

Coal Mine (Regulation and Industry) Acts (1842, 1872, 1908, 1911, 1920, 1930, 1938, 1994)

Coal Industry Nationalisation Act (1946)

Colliery Guardian and Coal Trades Yearbook (1947, 1955)

Dudley, D., *Metallum Martis* (1665, reprinted in facsimile, 1854)

Ede, J.F., *History of Wednesbury* (1962)

Erdeswick, S. and Harwood, T. (ed.), *A Survey of Staffordshire* (1844)

Francis, J.R., *A History of Cannock Chase Colliery Company* (1980)

Hackwood, F.W., *Oldbury and Round About* (1915)

Hackwood, F.W., *A History of West Bromwich* (1895)

Hair, P.E.H., 'Mortality in coal-mines, 1800-50', *Economic History Review* (1968)

Hurdcock, W.D. (ed.), *English Historical Documents, vol. xii (2) 1874-1914* (1977)

Industrial Archaeology (various volumes, including Francis, J.R., 'An early experiment in the use of electricity' (1971), and Griffin, A.B., 'Coalmining' (1971))

Illustrated London News (1873)

Inglestone, B., 'Modernising the coal industry', *Industrial World* (1929)

Journal of the Staffordshire Industrial Archaeological Society (1974, 1980)

Kelly's Directory of Staffordshire (various years)

Kirby, M.W., *The British Coalmining Industry 1870-1946* (1977)

Lones, T.E., *History of Mining in the Black Country* (1898)

Memoirs of the Geological Survey (1859, 1918, 1925)

Mining Journal (various volumes)

National Coal Board, *Plan for Coal* (1974)

North Staffordshire Journal of Field Studies (various volumes, including Jones, J.I., 'Licensed coalmining in North Staffordshire', vol. 9 (1969))

Peel, R., *Coal Mining* (1917 edn)

Penman, D. and Penman, J.S., *The Principles and Practice of Mine Ventilation* (1957 edn)

Pigot's Commercial Directory (various years)

Pitt, W., *A Topographical History of Staffordshire* (1817)

Plot, R., *The Natural History of Staffordshire* (1686)

Raybould, T.J., 'The development and organisation of Lord Dudley's mineral estates, 1774-1845', *Economic History Review* (1968)

Reports of HM Mines Inspectorate

Report of the Commission on South Staffordshire Drainage (1920)

Report of the Commission on the Employment of Children in Mines and Manufactories (1840)

Report of Midland District Valuation Board: West Cannock Colliery Co. Ltd (1950)

Report of the Midland Mining Commission (1843)

William Salt Library:
  Collections for a History of Staffordshire (various volumes)
  Evans, J., *collection of notes*, 21/66/2005
  Account books for Iron Works 1576-82, D1734

Scarfe, N., *The La Rochefoucault Brothers' Tour of England in 1785* (1995)

Shaw, S., *The History and Antiquities of Staffordshire* (1778)

Sherlock, R., *The Industrial Archaeology of Staffordshire* (1975)

Staffordshire Record Office:
Paget MS
Capital and shares Cannock Chase Colliery Company, D240/M/GA.L
Cannock Chase Colliery collection, D315/M/ BI
  Hammerwich and Uxbridge letter collection, D603 – CE
  State of roads due to coal carrying, Q/SR M 1699
  Receipts Beaudesert Park, D 1734/3/4/35
  Accounts 1641: Cannock Wood and Beaudesert Park, D1734/3/3/261
  Sinking a deep pit: 1600, D1734/3/3/255
  Report on the mines of the Earl of Dudley: Liddell and Smith D.260/M/F/5/19/2
  Electricity orders (Chasetown) Q/RUM 778 and Q/RJM 979

Staffordshire Mining Drainage Act (1873)

Staffordshire Studies (various volumes)

Sturgess, R.W., 'Land ownership and mining in nineteenth century Staffordshire' in Ward, J.T. and Wilson, R.G. (eds), *Land and Industry* (1971)

Taylor, A., *The Staffordshire Coal Industry* (1981)

The Blackcountryman (various volumes)

Toulmin Smith, L. (ed.), *The Itinerary of John Leland* (1907)

Transactions of the Institute of Mining Engineers (various volumes)

Transactions of the Newcomen Society (1968, 1970)

Transactions of the North Staffs Institute of Mining Engineers (various volumes)

Transaction of the South Staffordshire Archaeological and Historical Society (various volumes)

Trueman, A.E., *The Coalfields of Great Britain* (1954)

Universal British Directory (1793)

Victoria County History of the County of Staffordshire (vol. v, 1959; vol. vii, 1995; vol. viii, 1963; vol. xvii, 1976; vol. xx, 1984)

Wardle, W., *Reference Book on Practical Mining* (1889)

Wise, M.J. (ed.), *Birmingham and its Regional Setting* (1950)

www.bhills-history.fsnet.co.uk/coal_mining. htm

www.people.ex.ac.uk/pfclaugh/mhinf/ location.htm

www.staffspasttrack.org.uk

www.thepotteries.org

Back copies of *Colliery Guardian, Mining Journal, Cannock Advertiser, Dudley Chronicle, Express and Star, Midland Examiner and Wolverhampton Times, Staffordshire Advertiser, Staffordshire Sentinel, Wolverhampton Chronicle, Worcester Chronicle*

Further Reading

Belcher, S., *Cannock Chase Past* (2001)

Brook, F., *The Industrial Archaeology of the British Isles 1 The West Midlands* (1977)

Chapman, N.A., *A History of Coal Mining around Halesowen* (1999)

Chapman, N.A., *The South Staffordshire Coalfield* (2005)

Goddard, A., *Goodbye Old Pick* (2005)

Leigh, F., *Mining Memories* (1992)

Leigh, F., *Most Valiant of Men* (1993)

Noszlopy, G.T. and Waterhouse, F., *The Public Sculpture of Staffordshire and the Black Country* (2005)

Rowlands, M., *The West Midlands from A.D. 1000* (1987)

Sherlock, R.W., *The Industrial Archaeology of Staffordshire* (1976)

Index

Page numbers in **bold** type refer to illustrations